CRC SERIES IN RADIOTRACERS IN BIOLOGY AND MEDICINE

Editor-in-Chief

Lelio G. Colombetti, Sc.D.
Loyola University
Stritch School of Medicine
Maywood, Illinois

STUDIES OF CELLULAR FUNCTION USING RADIOTRACERS
Mervyn W. Billinghurst, Ph.D.
 Radiopharmacy
 Health Sciences Center
 Winnipeg, Manitoba, Canada

GENERAL PROCESSES OF RADIOTRACER LOCALIZATION
Leopold J. Anghileri, D.Sc.
 Laboratory of Biophysics
 University of Nancy
 Nancy, France

RADIATION BIOLOGY
Donald Pizzarello, Ph.D.
 Department of Radiology
 New York University Medical Center
 New York, New York

RADIOTRACERS FOR MEDICAL APPLICATIONS
Garimella V. S. Rayudu, Ph.D.
 Nuclear Medicine Department
 Rush University Medical Center
 Presbyterian-St. Luke's Hospital
 Chicago, Illinois

RECEPTOR-BINDING RADIOTRACERS
William C. Eckelman, Ph.D.
 Department of Radiology
 George Washington University School of
 Medicine
 Washington, D.C.

BIOLOGIC APPLICATIONS OF RADIOTRACERS
Howard J. Glenn, Ph.D.
 University of Texas System Cancer Center
 M.D. Anderson Hospital and Tumor
 Institute
 Houston, Texas

BIOLOGICAL TRANSPORT OF RADIOTRACERS
Lelio G. Colombetti, Sc.D.
 Loyola University
 Stritch School of Medicine
 Maywood, Illinois

BASIC PHYSICS OF RADIOTRACERS
W. Earl Barnes, Ph.D.
 Nuclear Medicine Service
 Edward Hines, Jr., Hospital
 Hines, Illinois

RADIOBIOASSAYS
Fuad S. Ashkar, M.D.
 Radioassay Laboratory
 Jackson Memorial Medical Center
 University of Miami School of Medicine
 Miami, Florida

COMPARTMENTAL DISTRIBUTION OF RADIOTRACERS
James S. Robertson, M.D., Ph.D.
 Mayo Medical School
 Mayo Clinic
 Rochester, Minnesota

RADIONUCLIDES PRODUCTION
Frank Helus, Sc.D.
 Institute of Nuclear Medicine
 German Cancer Research Center
 Heidelberg, Germany

Radionuclides Production

Volume I

Editor

Frank Helus, Sc.D.
Institute of Nuclear Medicine
German Cancer Research Center
Heidelberg, West Germany

Editor-inChief
CRC Series in Radiotracers in Biology
and Medicine

Lelio G. Colombetti, Sc.D.
Loyola University
Stritch School of Medicine
Maywood, Illinois

CRC Press, Inc.
Boca Raton, Florida

Library of Congress Cataloging in Publication Data
Main entry under title:

Radionuclides production.

(CRC series in radiotracers in biology and
medicine
Bibliography: p.
Includes index.
1. Radioisotopes. I. Helus, Frank. II. Series.
[DNLM: 1. Radioisotopes. 2. Nuclear physics--
Methods.   QC 795.7 R129]
QD601.2.R35   1983   621.48'37   83-2827
ISBN 0-8493-6003-X (v. 1)
ISBN 0-8493-6004-8 (v. 2)

International Standard Book Number 0-8493-6003-X (Vol.1)
International Standard Book Number 0-8493-6004-8 (Vol.2)

Library of Congress Card Number 83-2827
Printed in the United States

FOREWORD

This series of books on Radiotracers in Biology and Medicine is on the one hand an unbelievably expansive enterprise and on the other hand, a most noble one as well. Tools to probe biology have developed at an accelerating rate. Hevesy pioneered the application of radioisotopes to the study of chemical processes, and since that time, radioisotopic methodology has probably contributed as much as any other methodology to the analysis of the fine structure of biologic systems. Radioisotopic methodologies represent powerful tools for the determination of virtually any process of biologic interest. It should not be surprising, therefore, that any effort to encompass all aspects of radiotracer methodology is both desirable in the extreme and doomed to at least some degree of inherent failure. The current series is assuredly a success relative to the breadth of topics which range from in depth treatise of fundamental science or abstract concepts to detailed and specific applications, such as those in medicine or even to the extreme of the methodology for sacrifice of animals as part of a radiotracer distribution study. The list of contributors is as impressive as is the task, so that one can be optimistic that the endeavor is likely to be as successful as efforts of this type can be expected to be. The prospects are further enhanced by the unbounded energy of the coordinaing editor. The profligate expansion of application of radioisotopic methods relate to their inherent and exquisite sensitivity, ease of quantitation, specificity, and comparative simplicity, especially with modern instrumentation and reagents, both of which are now readily and universally available. It is now possible to make biological measurements which were otherwise difficult or impossible. These measurements allow us to begin to understand processes in depth in their unaltered state so that radioisotope methodology has proved to be a powerful probe for insight into the function and perturbations of the fine structure of biologic systems. Radioisotopic methodology has provided virtually all of the information now known about the physiology and pathophysiology of several organ systems and has been used abundantly for the development of information on every organ system and kinetic pathway in the plant and animal kingdoms. We all instinctively turn to the thyroid gland and its homeostatic interrelationships as an example, and an early one at that, of the use of radioactive tracers to elaborate normal and abnormal physiology and biochemistry, but this is but one of many suitable examples. Nor is the thyroid unique in the appreciation that a very major and important residua of diagnostic and therapeutic methods of clinical importance result from an even larger number of procedures used earlier for investigative purposes and, in some instances, procedures used earlier for investigative purposes and, in some instances, advocated for clinical use. The very ease and power of radioisotopic methodology tempts one to use these techniques without sufficient knowledge, preparation or care and with the potential for resulting disastrous misinformation. There are notable research and clinical illustrations of this problem, which serve to emphasize the importance of texts such as these to which one can turn for guidance in the proper use of these powerful methods. Radioisotopic methodology has already demonstrated its potential for opening new vistas in science and medicine. This series of texts, extensive though they be, yet must be incomplete in some respects. Multiple authorship always entails the danger of nonuniformity of quality, but the quality of authorship herein assembled makes this likely to be minimal. In any event, this series undoubtedly will serve an important role in the continued application of radioisotopic methodology to the exciting and unending, yet answerable, questions in science and medicine!

Gerald L. DeNardo, M.D.
Professor of Radiology, Medicine,
Pathology and Veterinary Radiology
University of California, Davis-
Sacramento Medical School
Director, Division of Nuclear Medicine

THE EDITOR-IN-CHIEF

Lelio G. Colombetti, Sc.D., is Professor of Pharmacology at Loyola University Stritch School of Medicine in Maywood, Ill. and a member of the Nuclear Medicine Division Staff at Michael Reese Hospital and Medical Center in Chicago, Ill.

Dr. Colombetti graduated from the Litoral University in his native Argentina with a Doctor in Sciences degree (summa cum laude), and obtained two fellowships for postgraduate studies from the Georgetown University in Washington, D.C., and from the M.I.T. in Cambridge, Mass. He has published more than 150 scientific papers and is the author of several book chapters. He has presented over 300 lectures both at meetings held in the U.S. and abroad. He organized the First International Symposium on Radiopharmacology, held in Innsbruck, Austria, in May 1978. He also organized the Second International Symposium on Radiopharmacology which took place in Chicago in September, 1981, with the active participation of more than 500 scientists, representing over 30 countries. He is a founding member of the International Association of Radiopharmacology, a nonprofit organization, which congregates scientists from many disciplines interested in the biological applications of radiotracers. He was its first President (1979/1981.

Dr. Colombetti is a member of various scientific societies, including the Society of Nuclear Medicine (U.S.) and the Gesellschaft für Nuklearmedizin (Europe), and is an honorary member of the Mexican Society of Nuclear Medicine. He is also a member of the Society of Experimental Medicine and Biology, the Coblenz Society, and the Sigma Xi. He is a member of the editorial boards of the journals *Nuklearmedizin* and *Research in Clinic and Laboratory*.

THE EDITOR

Frank Helus, Sc.D., is leading the radiochemistry group and is the person responsible for the production of cyclotron and reactor radionuclides at the Institute of Nuclear Medicine, German Cancer Research Center, Heidelberg. He studied nuclear chemistry and radiochemistry at Prague Charles University and the Technical University of Prague. He received his degree in nuclear chemistry from Technical University of Prague in 1960. After his studies he joined the academic staff at the Department of Nuclear Chemistry at the Technical University of Prague and conducted both theoretical (hot atom chemistry lecture) and practical classes for students. At the same time he made extensive research work in the field of the chemical behavior of the trace products after nuclear reactions. He moved to Italy in 1967, where he worked on the preparation of technetium labeled radiopharmaceuticals for medical use, and in 1969 he joined the Hammersmith Cyclotron Unit M.R.C. research group in London and began working on the production of cyclotron radionuclides. In 1971 he moved to Heidelberg where he is now in charge of the Radiochemical group with specific interests in the production and labeling processes with short-lived positron emitters and non-invasive physiological studies performed through the use of such nuclides.

Frank Helus is known for his research on the production of Br-77 and F-18 and is authority in the production of cyclotron radionuclides for medical use; more specifically in cyclotron targetry and fast separation procedures. His publications comprise more than 50 research papers. He is a member of various scientific societies.

CONTRIBUTORS

Zeev Alfassi, Ph.D.
Associate Professor
Nuclear Engineering Department
Ben Gurion University
Beer Sheva, Israel

R. E. Boyd, Ph.D.
Head, Radioactive Products
Research Section, Isotope Division
Australian Atomic Energy Commission
Research Establishment
Lucas Heights Research Laboratories
Sutherland, Australia

Frank Helus, Sc.D.
Institute of Nuclear Medicine
German Cancer Research Center
Heidelberg, West Germany

R. S. Mani, Ph.D.
Head
Radiopharmaceutical Section
Isotope Group
Bhabha Atomic Research Center
Bombay, India

Milorad Mladjenovic, Ph.D.
Professor
Boris Kidric Institute
University of Belgrade
Belgrade, Yugoslavia

Tadashi Nozaki, Ph.D.
Principal Scientist
Radiochemistry Laboratory
Rikagaku Kenkyu-sho
Saitama, Japan

A. M. J. Paans, Ph.D
Department of Nuclear Medicine
University Hospital
Groningen, The Netherlands

G. D. Robinson, Jr., Ph.D.
Research Associate Professor of Neurol-
  ogy and Radiology
Director, Medical Cyclotron Facility
University of Pennylvania
Philadelphia, Pennsylvania

E. L. Sattler, Ph.D.
Strahlenzentrum
Giessen, West Germany

David J. Silvester, Ph.D.
Head, Chemistry Section
Medical Research Council Cyclotron
  Unit
Hammersmith Hospital
London, England

W. Vaalburg, Ph.D.
Head, Cyclotron Radiopharmaceutical
  Group
Department of Nuclear Medicine
University Hospital
Groningen, The Netherlands

Gerd Wolber, Ph.D.
Head, Cyclotron Group
German Cancer Research Center
Heidelberg, West Germany

TABLE OF CONTENTS

Volume I

Volume II

Chapter 1

RADIOISOTOPE PRODUCTION: AN HISTORICAL INTRODUCTION*

D. J. Silvester

Early in 1898 Marie Sklodowska Curie completed the investigations which led her to believe that the uranium ore pitchblende might contain an element that was of considerably higher activity, in terms of the intensity of radiation it emitted, than uranium itself. The single step that we can therefore now recognize as initiating the history of radioisotope production was taken on April 14th of that same year, when Marie and her husband Pierre Curie ground up a 100 g sample of pitchblende and began their attempts to separate from it this possibly new element.

In carrying out their chemical separations they could use only the simple analytical procedures that were then being taught to undergraduate students by their colleague Gustave Bémont, but to measure the radiation emitted by their samples they had a sensitive tool in their newly developed ionization chamber and electrometer. Within a few months they succeeded in showing that pitchblende contained not just one, but two new elements, for which Marie coined the description "radioactive". The first of these resembled bismuth in its chemical behavior, though its sulfide was more volatile; this they named polonium, after the country of Marie's birth. The second was so like barium that even after a long series of fractional crystallizations they obtained only a partial separation; but its radioactivity was of such intensity that they called this new element radium.

Although the existence of radium was corroborated by the spectroscopic observations of another colleague, Eugène Demarçay, the Curies needed much bigger samples of both elements to be able to determine their atomic weights and thereby prove their existence unequivocally.

At that time the St. Joachimsthal mines in Bohemia were the main source of pitchblende, from which uranium was extracted to serve chiefly as a coloring agent for glass. Through the mediation of an acquaintance at the University of Vienna the Curies were able to obtain, for no more than the cost of transporting it to Paris, 100 kg of pitchblende residues. Upon its arrival, Marie Curie embarked on what may be regarded as the first large-scale operation in radioisotope production which yielded, after 4 years labor in a laboratory which was little more than a shed in the grounds of the Sorbonne, one tenth of a gram of radium.

Commercial production of radium followed quickly upon its discovery, a German firm of quinine manufacturers, Buchler of Braunschweig, being the first to offer it for sale. Initially, it was cheap — only about $1.50 per milligram in 1905 — despite the laborious refining procedure it required. Small quantities were used by scientists in their research on the phenomenon of radioactivity, but its chief application was in the manufacture of luminous paint. Later, when the therapeutic effect of radiation on tumors was recognized, demands for "radium therapy" sent the price soaring to a peak of $180 per milligram in 1914.

Uranium ores contain only tiny amounts of radium (at best about 100 mg per ton) and commercial production moved to new locations as richer ores were discovered, first in the U.S., then in the Congo, and finally in Canada. Even so, the total amount of radium ever

---

* Insistence on the use of "radionuclide" rather than "radioisotope" came later than the period covered here, during which radioisotopes were first discovered and production was initiated. For this reason, the earlier description is used throughout this article.

refined throughout the world by the time production ceased in the early 1950s was little more than 3 kg.

The radioactive transformation process was at first a very puzzling one to the many scientists who studied it in the first decade of this century. Radioactivity was recognized as an atomic property, yet as more and more naturally occurring radioactive species were discovered it became impossible to find a place for them all in the periodic table of elements — if indeed each were a new element. It was the chemist Frederick Soddy who in 1913 made coherent sense out of the wealth of data that had by then been accumulated, by proposing the theory of isotopes — i.e., that more than one atomic species could occupy the same place in the periodic table.

Almost at once, the important practical implications of this theory were demonstrated by George de Hevesy and Fritz Paneth who showed that minute amounts of RaD (which could now be recognized as a radioactive isotope of lead — ^{210}Pb) could be used as a radioactive tracer, or indicator, for lead in determining the solubilities of sparingly soluble lead salts. Paneth went on to develop the tracer technique in further studies in inorganic chemistry, but it was again Hevesy who, in 1923, first applied it to a biological problem when he investigated the uptake of lead by plants, using this time solutions containing ThB (^{212}Pb). Only a year later Blumgart and Weiss carried out the first clinical study with a radioactive tracer: by injecting RaC(^{212}Bi) into one arm, and detecting its arrival in the other arm by means of a cloud chamber, they measured blood circulation time and showed that this was increased in patients with heart disease.

While only naturally occurring radioactive isotopes were available the scope for their use as tracers was strictly limited, but this situation was to change dramatically in the next decade, following the discovery that radioisotopes could be produced artificially. It happened thus: in 1933, Marie Curie's daughter Irene, together with her husband Frederic Joliot, discovered that some light elements emitted positrons while being bombarded with the α-particles emitted from a polonium source. Continuing these studies, they were excited to observe that when an aluminum foil was so bombarded it continued to emit positrons for some time after the polonium source had been removed. By means of rapid chemical separations they ascertained that the radioactivity, which they found to have a half-life of 3.25 min, was due to the formation of a new radioactive isotope of phosphorus, ^{30}P.

They observed the same phenomenon when they bombarded boron or magnesium instead of aluminum, and believed that in doing so they had formed radionitrogen and radiosilicon, respectively. They concluded their publication of this work, in *Nature* on February 10, 1934, with the remarks: "These elements and similar ones may possibly be formed in different nuclear reactions with other bombarding particles: protons, deutrons, (sic) neutrons. For example, $_7$N^{13} could perhaps be formed by the capture of a deutron in $_6$C^{12}, followed by the emission of a neutron."

When he read this paper some days later, 6000 miles from Paris in Berkeley, California, Ernest Lawrence was immediately struck by the irony of those concluding remarks. Just a few years previously, Lawrence had conceived the idea of the cyclotron as a device to accelerate charged particles to high velocities. His objective in doing so was to extend the study of nuclear reactions beyond the range of those that could be induced by the α-particles emitted by natural radioactive sources.

By 1934 Lawrence had built a cyclotron capable of accelerating deuterons to about 3-MeV and had been joined by a team of hard-working enthusiasts, anxious to find out all that could be done with this exciting new machine. They used a Geiger counter to monitor the radiation generated when the cyclotron was operating, and at the time no doubt it seemed sensible that machine and counter should be on the same electrical circuit. Had it been otherwise, however, they could hardly have failed to notice that their cyclotron targets remained radioactive after the cyclotron was switched off — and artificial radioactivity would surely first have been discovered in California, not Paris!*

As it was, Lawrence's team quickly rearranged their wiring and set about bombarding a carbon target with the cyclotron's deuteron beam. Just as Joliot and Curie had predicted, when the beam was switched off the target was observed to be radioactive, with a half-life of 10 min attributable to the formation of ^{13}N.

Following this first experiment, the path was open to the discovery and production, using Lawrence's cyclotron, of many more artificial radioisotopes in the next few years. In 1934, however, events were moving swiftly in other parts of the world as well.

In Rome, Enrico Fermi had also read the Joliot and Curie paper and decided to see if new radioisotopes could be made by neutrons. He and his collaborators realized that neutrons, unlike α-particles and other charged particles, would be neither scattered by electrons nor repelled by the Coulomb barrier around the atomic nucleus, and so quite low energy neutrons might induce nuclear reactions in even the heaviest target nuclei. Since such things could not be bought in 1934 they learned first how to make their own Geiger counter; then they learned how to make a suitable neutron source, by sealing up radon (^{222}Rn) with beryllium powder in a glass vial. Only then were they ready to start their experiments.

Fermi decided upon a systematic approach. Starting with hydrogen he planned that they should work their way through the periodic table, bombarding as many elements as they could lay their hands on. From hydrogen to oxygen no radioactivity was observed in their targets, but in the ninth element, fluorine, their hopes were fulfilled. In the weeks which followed they bombarded some 60 elements, and found that radioactivity could be induced in about 40 of them. They made the further observation that the lighter elements (i.e., those with $Z<30$) were usually transmuted into radioisotopes of a chemically different element, whereas heavier elements appeared to yield radioisotopes of the same element as the target.

News of these discoveries spread rapidly around the scientific community, so that by September Leo Szilard, who at that time was working at St. Bartholomew's Hospital in London with T. A. Chalmers, was able to propose a new principle by which radioisotopes could be separated from targets of the same element. In their own words which appeared in *Nature* on 22 September 1934: "If we irradiate by a neutron source a chemical compound of the element in which we are interested, we might expect those atoms of the element which are struck by a neutron to be removed from the compound. Whether the atoms freed in this way will interchange with their isotopes bound in the irradiated chemical compound will depend on the nature of the chemical compound with which we have to deal."

As a practical demonstration of this principle, Szilard and Chalmers showed that radioiodine could easily be recovered as inorganic iodide from irradiated ethyl iodide, by simply extracting it from the organic liquid with water.

Although of limited application, this so-called "Szilard-Chalmers effect" has subsequently been of considerable practical value in the production of a few radioisotopes such as ^{51}Cr and ^{64}Cu.

In Rome, meanwhile, Fermi's group were making a further discovery. One morning they found when they were bombarding silver with neutrons that the intensity of the radioactivity they induced depended upon the environment surrounding their neutron source and target. Investigating this more closely, they found that interposing a sheet of lead between source and target slightly increased the induced radioactivity, but a sheet of paraffin wax enormously increased it.

* In discussion with the author in 1981, John Lawrence (Ernest's physician brother) told this story a little differently. He said that it had been noticed that the Geiger counter continued to click after the cyclotron beam was switched off (implying that it was already wired separately) but that this was attributed to a fault in the instrument.

Fermi produced a theoretical explanation while his colleagues were at lunch: paraffin wax consists very largely of hydrogen atoms, and these would be more effective than any other atoms at slowing down the high-velocity neutrons emerging from a radon-beryllium source. Furthermore, slow neutrons would be more likely to be captured by the target nuclei, and this was presumed to be the prerequisite to the formation of radioisotopes.

Fermi's theory was put to the test the same afternoon. Another substance consisting largely of hydrogen atoms is water, and there was a large body of water near at hand in the goldfish pond just behind their laboratory. When Fermi and his colleagues trooped outside and immersed their neutron source and silver target in the pond they soon found that, as predicted, water was just as effective as paraffin wax had been at increasing the radioactivity induced in silver.

One of the earliest artificial radioisotopes to be discovered by Fermi's group was ^{32}P, and this was certainly one of the first to be used extensively as a radioactive tracer. Again it was Hevesy who showed the way. In 1935, working now with Chievitz in Copenhagen where Niels Bohr provided them with a neutron source, he studied the uptake and elimination of ^{32}P-phosphate in the various tissues of rats, and demonstrated for the first time the constant turnover of one of the vital chemical constituents of living creatures.

Studies of this type were soon initiated in other parts of the world, and built up great demand for radioisotopes to use as tracers. Important though neutron sources were in the discovery of new radioisotopes (of which over 100 had been identified by the end of 1935) the quantities they could generate were tiny compared to the output from a cyclotron, so it was the latter which was to remain the dominant supplier for practical applications until the mid-1940s. Indeed, constant improvements to the original Berkeley cyclotron meant that by December 1936 John Lawrence could obtain sufficient ^{32}P to initiate its use in therapy of leukemia patients — earlier tracer experiments having indicated its probable effectiveness.

Among other radioisotopes that were found to be particularly valuable as metabolic tracers in those early days, ^{128}I deserves special mention. It could be made conveniently either by using a neutron-source and the Szilard-Chalmers effect, mentioned above, or by bombarding targets containing iodine with a deuteron beam from a cyclotron. Its drawback was its short (25 min) half-life. John Lawrence pointed out that (at that time) the ideal radioisotope of iodine for thyroid studies would have a half-life of about a week, and an intensive search was soon rewarded when Livingood and Seaborg discovered ^{131}I(8d) in tellurium targets which they had bombarded with deuterons.

Iodine-131 soon displaced ^{128}I in the diagnosis and study of thyroid disorders, and when virtually unlimited supplies became available at the end of World War II it was for many years the most widely used tracer in medical science.

Another of the earliest radioisotopes discovered using the Berkeley cyclotron, ^{11}C, was also of special practical importance since carbon is, of course, a fundamental element in the chemistry of life. Carbon-11 has a half-life of only 20 min, but it was not difficult to make in good yields by bombarding targets containing boron with a deuteron beam, and it could easily be recovered in the form of CO_2. By setting up a chemical laboratory close to the cyclotron, Martin Kamen was able to synthesize a remarkable variety of organic compounds labeled wth ^{11}C, and even succeeded in demonstrating biosynthetic reactions, such as the photosynthesis of sugars by plant leaves which he exposed to the radioactive CO_2.

However, ^{11}C was clearly too short-lived to serve as a tracer in any but the most rapid biochemical reactions, and many people began searching for a longer-lived radioisotope of carbon. It must be said that according to the nuclear theory current at that time they had little hope of a successful outcome, since it was predicted that even the best bet, ^{14}C, would most probably have a half-life of less than 1 sec. Nevertheless, the reward being so high, in 1939 Kamen and Ruben joined the search, and after some months were successful in producing weak radioactivity, attributable to ^{14}C, from the ^{13}C(d,p) reaction in a graphite target that they had bombarded for a total of 4800 μAh with 7 MeV deuterons. They repeated the experiment with graphite enriched in ^{13}C, and noted an increased yield of radioactivity, the half-life of which was calculated to be of the order of 10^3 years.

Not long afterwards, quite by chance, they found the same product in a large bottle of ammonium nitrate solution which had been standing near the cyclotron, and in which it had been formed by the $^{14}N(n,p)$ reaction. They found that the ^{14}C made in this way could easily be recovered merely by blowing air through the solution and oxidizing the resultant radioactive vapor to CO_2. Furthermore, the rate of production was very much greater by this route than by deuteron bombardment of graphite, and clearly could be developed as a cheap method of producton.

At about the same time, again using the Berkeley cyclotron, Alvarez and Cornog discovered tritium in water which had been bombarded with deuterons. Thus, in Martin Kamen's words: "within a few months after the scientific world had somewhat ruefully concluded that development of tracer techniques would be seriously handicapped because useful radioactive tracers for carbon, hydrogen, oxygen, and nitrogen did not exist, ^{14}C and ^{3}H were discovered, and the situation greatly improved".

Indeed it might be said that the enormous advances in the field of biochemistry of the last few decades owe more to the availability of ^{14}C and ^{3}H labeled tracers than to any other factor.

Notwithstanding the value of nuclear physics research that had been carried out with the early cyclotrons, it was their contribution to medical research, through the generation of radioactive isotopes, that was of the greatest help to Ernest Lawrence in raising funds with which to build a larger cyclotron. The 60-in cyclotron, capable of accelerating deuterons to about 20 MeV, which was completed in 1939 was known from its conception as the "medical cyclotron", and was indeed a prolific source of radioisotopes. However, within a few years the volume of its output (and that of the several other cyclotrons which had been built elsewhere by then) was totally eclipsed by the primitive nuclear reactors — called at the time "atomic piles" — which were hastily developed as part of the U.S. war effort, following the discovery of nuclear fission in 1939.

Just as, with the benefit of hindsight, we can say that artificial radioisotopes ought to have been discovered by Ernest Lawrence, so we can say that nuclear fission ought to have been discovered by Enrico Fermi — but it was not.

In 1934, Fermi's group was the first to expose uranium to bombardment by slow neutrons, and to observe that several activities could be detected as a consequence. One of them could presumably be attributed to ^{239}U, produced by the (n,γ) reaction, but the problem of accounting for the others occupied several brilliant minds, including those of Irene Joliot-Curie and P. Savitch in Paris, and Otto Hahn, Lise Meitner, and F. Strassmann in Berlin, for the next 4 years.

Eventually it was Hahn and Strassmann who, having taken the utmost pains over their radiochemical analyses, concluded that the only explanation for their observations was to postulate that the neutron-bombarded uranium atoms underwent fission into two fragments, each of roughly similar mass.

Fermi, now in Chicago, assembled the first atomic pile in 1942, to demonstrate the feasibility of initiating a self-sustaining chain-reaction in which ^{255}U underwent neutron-induced fission, generating more neutrons in the process. Subsequently, piles were built at Oak Ridge, Tennessee, and Hanford, Washington, for the purpose of making ^{239}Pu (for atomic weapons) by neutron-capture in ^{238}U.

The "pile" was thus a copious source of low-energy neutrons which as well as manufacturing plutonium could produce what were hitherto enormous quantities of radioisotopes from reactions such as (n,f), (n,γ), and (n,p), and once the war was over the U.S. authorities lost little time in deciding to make these radioisotopes available "for peaceful and humanitarian ends".

The announcement of this decision, in *Science* on 14th June 1946, made it clear that to begin with distribution was to be restricted to qualified institutions within the U.S. Priority would be given first to fundamental scientific research, then to therapeutic, diagnostic, or tracer studies, next to training and education in radioisotope techniques, and finally to research in applied science.

What was offered was a range of fission products, though, because of the difficulties of separating these, few were available as individual species: most were in mixtures of perhaps four or five radioisotopes. In addition, some nonfission radioisotopes were available: 58 low specific-activity products of (n,γ) reactions were listed, but, most important, a few so-called "carrier-free" products were offered, and these included ^{14}C, ^{32}P, ^{35}S, and ^{131}I.

The first shipment of a radioisotope, following this announcement, was made on 2nd August 1946, when a 1 mCi sample of ^{14}C (as $BaCO_3$) was sent from the Oak Ridge laboratories to a hospital in St. Louis, Missouri, and in the following 12 months more than 1100 further shipments were made of which 99 were ^{14}C samples, 261 were ^{32}P, and 313 were ^{131}I.

These last figures show that demand was greatest for those radioisotopes which the earliest reactors (to give them from now on their modern name) were least well-equipped to produce, since their production required the introduction of "foreign" target materials into the reactor. Reactors built later took this into account, and were consequently better able to meet the burgeoning demand.

The U.S. Atomic Energy Commission, which came into being on 1st January 1947, took over the isotope distribution program and in September that year announced its readiness to ship radioisotopes to other countries. At the same time they published, in *Nucleonics* (September 1947), their second catalogue of radioisotopes on offer, and this time included prices. Formerly, prices had been adjusted to cover operational costs, and on this basis early shipments of ^{14}C cost about $367 per mCi. Now, however, demand for this radioisotope being so high, its price could be reduced to $50 per mCi. Other prices quoted were: ^{32}P $1.10 per mCi; ^{35}S $35 per mCi; and ^{131}I $1.70 per mCi.

Although several countries were quick to take advantage of the U.S. export arrangements, those that were in a position to do so, such as the United Kingdom, France, and Canada, were also busy developing their own reactors and radioisotope production facilities. For example at Harwell in the U.K. small samples of ^{32}P and ^{131}I were first produced in September 1947, and a year later the availability of "British" radioisotopes for clinical research was announced in the medical press.

An even more significant event took place in 1948, however, when, at the Ohio State University Hospital, reactor-produced ^{60}Co was first used in place of radium as a radiation source in the treatment of cancer. It was W. G. Myers who first drew attention to the advantages that would accrue from substituting this artificial radioisotope for the naturally occurring one, and more than any other event the implementation of his suggestion was responsible for the demise of the radium refining industry. Cobalt-60 could be manufactured by the ton in reactors whereas (as we stated earlier) the total world production of radium never exceeded much more than 3 kg.

Nuclear reactors thus made radioisotopes for use as tracers and radiation sources available for the first time on a world-wide scale and at not unreasonable cost. However, by 1949 murmurings in favor of cyclotrons as sources of radioisotopes began once more to be heard. It was pointed out that cyclotrons could produce a range of neutron-deficient radioisotopes not available from neutron-induced reactions, and that their scope for the production of "carrier-free" radioisotopes was far greater than that of reactors. Some of these were of course available from the numerous cyclotrons that had been built in the 1930s and 1940s for research in nuclear physics, but the A.E.C. decided to build a new machine at Oak Ridge for the prime purpose of radioisotope production.

This 22-MeV proton machine began operating in 1950. It was unique in having vertical "dees", and was capable of operating at currents up to several milliamps. Although these particular features have not been reproduced elsewhere as yet, this machine was the forerunner of the many cyclotrons that have since been built for commercial radioisotope production.

Despite always being referred to as the "medical cyclotron", the machine Ernest Lawrence had built at Berkeley in 1939 was in fact several miles from the nearest major hospital, which was across the bay in San Francisco. It was the British Medical Research Council that in 1946 took the decision to build a cyclotron for the first time right inside a teaching hospital. This decision was based partly on the need for such a machine for research in radiobiology and radiotherapy, but also on the fact that it would then become possible to undertake clinical research with short-lived radioisotopes, such as 2 min half-life ^{15}O or 10 min half-life ^{13}N, which it would be impossible to obtain from any distance. The advantages to be gained by using short-lived rather than long-lived radioisotopes in clinical work were threefold:

1. The total radiation dose to the patient would be lower.
2. For a given radiation dose, higher initial activities could be used, and so the data obtained should be more accurate.
3. With a short-lived radioisotope, serial measurements could be carried out with no buildup of background activity.

This cyclotron, which was built at Hammersmith Hospital London, began operating in 1955 and within a few years began to demonstrate the advantages that had been predicted, and an important additional one that had not. Many of the short-lived radioisotopes it produced were positron emitters, and these could be located in vivo and quantified with considerable accuracy by using a pair of scintillation counters to detect the coincident, "back-to-back", annihilation radiation quanta. Using this principle, which was to be developed over the next 20 years into the modern positron-emission tomographic scanners, much was quickly added to our knowledge of human physiology. For example, using ^{15}O-labeled oxygen and carbon dioxide gases, regional variations in the ventilation and perfusion of the lungs were demonstrated for the first time.

In general, of course, short-lived radioisotopes can only be used in close proximity to their source, be that a reactor or a cyclotron. Fortunately for the development of nuclear medicine, however, there is another way in which a limited number can be made more widely available. Whenever a long-lived radioisotope decays to form a shorter-lived radioactive daughter, and a suitable means can be found of separating daughter from parent, the latter can serve as a transportable source of the daughter radioisotope.

This general principle had been employed by radiologists since 1920, when Gioacchino Failla first prepared an intensive radiation source by encapsulating gaseous $^{222}Rn(3.8d)$ which he had extracted from its parent, the precious $^{226}Ra(1600y)$. In 1951, however, this principle was applied for the first time to the preparation of an artificial radioisotope, $^{132}I(2.3 h)$, for use as a diagnostic agent.

On 22nd February 1951 some 100 mCi of $^{132}Te(77h)$ were isolated from a fission-product mixture by Winsche, Stang, and Tucker at Brookhaven National Laboratory, New York. In *Nucleonics* of March that year they described their proposals for shipping this material, and for recovering the daughter ^{132}I, and 30 years later this makes fascinating reading:

"The parent tellurium will be dissolved in a eutectic mixture of lithium chloride and potassium chloride and shipped as a solid solution (melting point, 365°C). As the tellurium decays, the iodine produced also remains fixed in the solid salt mixture.

The vessel containing this salt mixture is called the "generator". Around it is built a thermostat-controlled electric heater, which, when turned on, will melt the contents. The generator will be placed inside a specially designed shipping shield and will remain in it during use. By applying suction to an outlet tube connected to the generator, air may be bubbled through the molten liquid sweeping out all of the iodine present, i.e., all that had grown in since the last such sweeping process minus that which had decayed to stable xenon.''

Had generator systems remained as complex as this it is very doubtful whether they would ever have achieved much more than academic interest. As it was, the gradual development of simpler methods of recovering ^{132}I culminated, in 1958, in the first use of an alumina chromatographic column to effect the separation of parent and daughter.

This particular generator enjoyed only a brief popularity, mainly in European medical centers, where ^{132}I was preferred to ^{131}I for thyroid studies; but another generator system, again utilizing an alumina column to separate parent and daughter, was also announced from Brookhaven at this time, and this one was destined to become perhaps the most widely used tool in the history of nuclear medicine. It was, of course, the ^{99}Mo-^{99m}Tc generator.

We have now reached the point at which this historical introduction must be concluded. Many aspects of radioisotope production, it is true, have not been mentioned, such as the use of accelerators other than cyclotrons, and especially the use of spallation reactions, the potential importance of which was foreseen as long ago as 1948. But these and other topics are part of the continuing development of radioisotope production which must properly be left to the following chapters of this book.

ACKNOWLEDGMENTS

In addition to original papers, a few of which are mentioned specifically in the text, I have drawn on the works of numerous authors in preparing this brief history. One, however, must be singled out for special mention: he is Wm. G. Myers of Ohio State University, himself a distinguished pioneer in the discovery, and application to medicine, of what he persistently calls "twinkling atoms". Now official historian to the U.S. Society of Nuclear Medicine, his essays (one written in collaboration with Henry N. Wagner, Jr., of Johns Hopkins University) are an invaluable starting point for anyone venturing into this field. These, and other sources, are listed below.

REFERENCES

1. **Davis, N. P.,** *Lawrence and Oppenheimer,* Simon and Schuster, New York, 1968.
2. **Fermi, L.,** *Atoms in the Family,* George Allen and Unwin, London, 1955.
3. **Glasstone, S.,** *Sourcebook on Atomic Energy,* Macmillan, London, 1956.
4. **Gowing, M.,** *Independence and Deterrence: Britain and Atomic Energy 1945—1952,* Vol. 2, Macmillan, London, 1974, chap. 20.
5. **Grove, W. P.,** Products of the newer alchemy, *Br. J. Radiol.,* 35, 725, 1962.
6. **Hevesy, G.,** Marie Curie and her contemporaries, *J. Nucl. Med.,* 2, 169, 1961.
7. **Jungk, R.,** Brighter Than 1000 Suns, *Penguin Books,* Harmondsworth, England, 1960.
8. **Kamen, M. D.,** *Isotopic Tracers in Biology,* Academic Press, New York, 1957.
9. **Martin, J. A., Livingston, R.S., Murray, R.L., and Rankin, M.,** Radioisotope production rates in a 22-MeV cyclotron, *Nucleonics,* 13, 28, 1955.
10. **McMillan, E. M.,** Particle accelerators, in *Experimental Nuclear Physics,* Vol. 3, Segre E., Ed., John Wiley & Sons, New York, 1959, chap 12.
11. **Myers, W. G.,** Becquerel's discovery of radioactivity in 1896, *J. Nucl. Med.,* 17, 579, 1976.

12. **Myers, W. G. and Wagner, H. N., Jr.,** Nuclear medicine: how it began, *Hospital Practice,* 9, 103, 1974.
13. **Newbery, G. R.,** Cyclotron-produced isotopes in clinical and experimental medicine, *Br. J. Radiol.,* 32, 633, 1959.
14. **Richards, P.,** Nuclide generators, in *Radioactive Pharmaceuticals,* Andrews, G. A., Kniseley, R. M., and Wagner, H. N., Jr., Eds., U.S. A.E.C. Divn. of Technical Information, 1966, chap. 10.
15. **Romer, A.,** *Radiochemistry and the Discovery of Isotopes,* Dover Publications, Inc., New York, 1970.
16. **Rutherford, L.,** Mme Curie, *Nature (London),* 134, 90, 1934.
17. **Seaborg, G. T.,** The preparation of radioactive isotopes, in *Proc. Symposium on the use of isotopes in biology and medicine,* University of Wisconsin, Madison, 1948, 43.

Chapter 2

NUCLEAR PHYSICS FUNDAMENTALS

Milorad Mladjenovic

TABLE OF CONTENTS

I. INTRODUCTION

A. Stability and Change of Atomic Structures

1. Types of Instability

The physical world can be considered as a hierarchy of structures. In physics we start from so-called elementary particles, which themselves have a complex internal hierarchy, and consider structures of atomic nucleus, atom as a whole, molecule, and solid state. A given structure is characterized, in the first approximation by its constituents and the energy involved to bind them and keep them together, called *binding energy* E_B.

An important property of physical structures, from particles to molecules, is the identity of all the systems of a given type. All the atoms of oxygen, for instance, are absolutely identical, and for that reason their binding energies have the same *constant* value.

A hierarchy of structures implies that its members are not absolutely stable. Any structure can be changed, partially damaged, or broken, when receiving from outside an appropriate amount of energy.

A *break up* occurs when the amount of energy received is higher than the binding energy. The nucleus of deuterium, for instance, breaks when it absorbs a photon of energy higher than $E_B = 2.2$ MeV, and one free proton and one free neutron are obtained.

If the energy available to a system from a passing or entering particle is lower than its total binding energy, but higher than the binding energy of its constituents, one or more of them can be ejected from the system. The simplest example is the ejection of an electron orbiting around the nucleus of an atom, a process called *ionization*.

When the available energy is not sufficient to expel the constituent affected by the incoming particle, a rearrangement of the structure can take place, and the process is called *inelastic collision or scattering*. The available energy is kept within the system, which is not any more in its stable state, but in one of its possible, discrete *excited states*. It is a characteristic of atomic systems that as a rule, which has some exceptions, they stay a very short time in the excited state. In the *deexcitation* process, the excess energy is disposed of, usually by emission of one or more photons.

In the experiments we use particle beams to bombard the atomic systems. A group of such particles can excite almost simultaneously many systems. An important characteristic of atomic structures is that a large number of systems excited at the same time do not get deexcited simultaneously. (It is like men born the same day, they do not die the same day). The deexcitation is a *statistical process*. All the identical systems, brought to the identical excited state, have the same *probability of deexcitation* in a given time interval. It means that in a unit time, such as a second, only a part of the total number of excited system shall make a transition to the stable state. In the next second again a part shall decay, but now their number will be smaller, because after the first second there are less excited systems left. In the following time intervals smaller and smaller numbers shall be decaying. When we plot the number of decays per unit time, an exponential curve is obtained. It is a natural curve representing many processes in nature and society.

An exponential curve does not end abruptly, but joins asymptotically the time axis. There is no other way to end, for a curve governed by statistics. In such a case the deexcitation or decay time is characterized by the time necessary for a half of a total number of excited systems to decay, which is called *half-life*.

The half-life of a given excited system depends on its physical properties and can vary by orders of magnitude from one case to another.

The excited states produced by inelastic collision represent only one of possible kinds of instability. Another important kind is obtained by capture of a particle, a process which can take place in the atomic nucleus. When a stable nucleus captures a neutron, for instance, the new nucleus is not a stable one. As a matter of fact there is a twofold instability. First, by including a new constituent into a well-bound system an amount of energy is liberated, which is equivalent to the energy necessary for its removal. That energy brings the nucleus into an excited state. The deexcitation takes place rather quickly, and then the nucleus is left in another kind of instability, due to relative numbers of protons and neutrons. The transition to stability can take place by a neutron transforming into proton, or vice versa. The excess energy is carried away by the emission of a beta-particle and extremely pene- trating, almost undetectable neutrino. This process is, perhaps, incorrectly called *radioactive beta decay*. The new nucleus is usually, but not always stable. If it is left, after beta emission, in the unexcited, ground state, it represents a *pure beta decay*. More often it is left in an excited state, and emits very quickly a few photons called *gamma rays*.

Radioactive decay is also a deexcitation process regulated by statistics and characterized by half-life.

The temporary excitation, permanent transformation, or break-up are types of changes which can happen to all the three important atomic structures or its parts: molecule, electron cloud around the atomic nucleus, and the nucleus itself.

A given type of nucleus determined by the number of protons and the number of neutrons is called a *nuclide*.

2. Stable Nuclides in Nature

There is a limited number of nuclides which do not show any spontaneous changes. We define as stable those nuclei in which no spontaneous change can be detected by the most sensitive measuring techniques available. The present limit of half-lives which can be meas- ured is in the best cases 10^{24} years, and any nuclear species disintegrating with longer half- lives are considered as stable.

The stable nuclides start from the simplest one, the hydrogen (A = 1, Z = 1), and end up with bismuth (A = 209, Z = 83), Due to improvement of measuring technique, their number has decreased to 265. The fact that there is no stable nuclei beyond bismuth is explained by the repulsive forces between positively charged protons. As their number increases, the electrical repulsion increases even faster, so that the stability of nuclei de- creases. For heavy nuclei beyond bismuth, the binding nuclear forces are not strong enough to overcome the electrical repulsion between protons.

The repulsive electrical forces between protons are responsible for another property of stable nuclides, related to relative number of neutrons and protons. In the light stable nuclei the number of neutrons is either equal to the number of protons, or very slightly higher, but from calcium (Z = 20) the number of neutrons is always higher. For the heaviest stable nuclides, the ratio of neutrons to protons is around 1.5 (Figure 1).

A survey of stable nuclides shows that the stability depends on the parity of nucleons. The largest number of stable nuclides have an even number of protons and neutrons, much less have an even number of either protons or neutrons, and only a few have odd number of both (Table 1).

A given element may have several stable nuclides, differing by the number of neutrons, which are called *isotopes*. If the number of protons is odd, there are usually one or two stable isotopes, while for even parity their number is larger, and may go up to ten. The measurements have shown that the proportions of various isotopes are constant and in general do not depend on the origin of a sample. These proportions are referred to as relative abundances or, in brief, as the *abundances,* and are expressed in percentages. We reproduce in Table 2 the relative abundances of tin, which has ten isotopes, more than any other nuclide.

The rule of constant abundances has some exceptions, which can be explained by certain natural enrichment processes. The best known examples are such gases as hydrogen, oxygen,

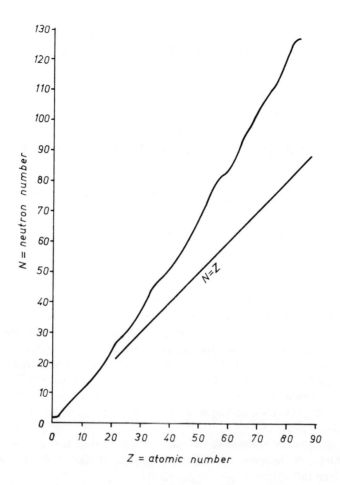

FIGURE 1.   The ratio of neutrons to protons for stable nuclides compared
to the case when their numbers are equal, $N = Z$.

Table 1
PARITY OF STABLE NUCLIDES

		Number of protons, Z	
		Even	**Odd**
Number of neutrons N	Even	155	49
	Odd	55	5

helium, and carbon, whose abundances can depend on environment. Another kind of abundance variation can be due to the presence of a naturally radioactive series.

The abundances have to be taken into account when ordering radioactive sources. The normal irradiation samples contain all the nuclides of a given element, so that several radioactive nuclides are simultaneously produced. In special cases isotopically enriched samples can be ordered for irradiation.

The constancy of relative abundances indicates a common origin of elements in universe.

Table 2
THE RELATIVE ABUNDANCE OF STABLE NUCLIDES OF TIN (Z = 50)

Mass number, A	112	114	115	116	117	118	119	120	122	124
Abundance, %	1.01	0.67	0.38	14.8	7.75	24.3	8.6	32.4	4.56	5.64

Table 3
THE NATURALLY RADIOACTIVE NUCLIDES WITH LONGEST HALF-LIVES (IN YEARS)

^{128}Te — 1.5×10^{24}	^{186}Os — 2×10^{15}	^{152}Gd — 1.1×10^{14}	^{190}Pt — 6×10^{11}
^{130}Te — 2×10^{21}	^{144}Nd — 2.1×10^{15}	^{115}In — 5.1×10^{14}	^{147}Sm — 1.1×10^{11}
^{82}Se — 1.4×10^{20}	^{148}Sm — 8×10^{15}	^{180}Ta — 1×10^{13}	^{187}Re — 4×10^{10}
^{174}Hf — 2×10^{15}	^{113}Cd — 9×10^{15}	^{138}La — 1.1×10^{11}	^{238}U — 4.5×10^{9}

3. Unstable Nuclides

There are now over 2300 known unstable nuclides, which can be divided into two groups according to their origin. A relatively smaller number of them can be found in nature, disintegrating at a very slow rate, with half-lives comparable or smaller than the age of elements. The products of radioactive disintegration, which can have various, usually shorter half-lives, are found with them. The best known are the three naturally radioactive series, with long-lived parents: uranium (U-238, 4.5×10^9 years), thorium (Th 232, 1.4×10^{10} years), and actinouranium (U-235, 7.1×10^8 years). Each series contain about 15 nuclides (18, 13, and 15, respectively), ending with one of the stable isotopes of lead (Pb 206, Pb 208, and Pb 207, respectively).

The remaining naturally radioactive nuclides are lighter than lead and are covering the whole periodic table of elements. Some of the longest lived ones (with half-lives measured in years) are given in Table 3.

For most of the practical work, these nuclides can be considered as stable, and standard periodic table of natural element ends with uranium, although its most abundant isotope disintegrates with a half-life of 4.5×10^9 years.

The artificially unstable nuclides can also be divided into two groups. One consists of new elements heavier than uranium. Fifteen transuranium elements have been produced so far (up to Z = 107), and more of them might be found. As one should expect, their instability is increasing, so that those beyond Z = 102 have half-lives of a few minutes or less. The increased instability is responsible for a mode of disintegration which is characteristic for transuranium region — the spontaneous fission. There are about 70 nuclides from thorium to nobelium (Z = 102), which can undergo a spontaneous fission, with half-lives ranging from 10^{21} years to a few milliseconds, at the heavier end. Only some nuclides from four elements beyond plutonium (up to californium) are used in practice. The heavier ones are too expensive to produce.

Most of the known unstable nuclides (over 1800) are lighter than bismouth. There are on the average nearly 20 radioactive nuclides per element. Their number is smaller for very light nuclei and largest for medium nuclei.

II. PARTICLES, FORCES, AND SYSTEMS

A. Elementary Particles

The constituent particles of the atom were said to be elementary as long as only a few elementary particles were known. After World War II the number of known elementary particles began to increase rapidly, so that at present there are hundreds of them. The term "elementary" is no longer adequate, but we shall use it nevertheless, since it will have a definite meaning in our considerations, limited to low energy phenomena. Namely, we shall dwell only on those particles which can be used for description of radioactive decay and ordinary natural phenomena. In radioactive decays, amounts of energy less than a few millions of electron volts are usually released, and only very rarely the emitted energy rises up to about 10 MeV. Still smaller energies are characteristic of the structure of atoms and molecules, and of the processes taking place in these. We can put aside the unstable particles produced by energy expenditure larger than 100 MeV.

Low energy phenomena can be described by means of the following elementary particles: nucleons (protons and neutrons), electrons, neutrinos, and photons. Atomic nuclei are composed of nucleons, while atomic shells consist of electrons. Changes in the energy of these systems are accompanied by absorption or emission of photons. The neutrino appears in beta decays, where one of the nucleons transforms into the other by emission of an electron and a neutrino.

Two particles in the list can appear, even at low energies, in two forms — as the particle and its antiparticle. These are the electron and the neutrino.

While there are only negative electrons in atomic shells, both negative and positive electrons may arise in beta decay or in specific electromagnetic processes. Both kinds of electrons have the same mass and carry a unit charge, but differ from each other in the sign of their charges. Only the negative electron is stable in the world we know. The positrons lives are brief, just the time needed to loose their kinetic energy, and are annihilated in encounters with negative electrons, with a release of energy equivalent to two electron rest masses.

The neutrino cannot be distinguished from the antineutrino by the sign of their charges, since both are neutral, but they differ from each other in their intrinsic angular moments. From the viewpoint of classical physics, it might be said that the neutrino "rotates" counterclockwise with respect to its direction of motion, whereas the antineutrino rotates clockwise.

The antiproton and the antineutron are unstable particles produced at very high energies. The photon occupies a special place in the classification of particles, and has no corresponding antiparticle. Hence, in total, seven elementary particles are sufficient for a description of low-energy phenomena.

The basic properties of elementary particles are characterized by their rest mass, charge, intrisic angular momentum (spin), and half-life. Another class of properties is regulating their possible changes, since elementary particles can be transformed, produced, annihilated, and bound into systems by the action of several kinds of forces. Now, any change in our world has to obey some conservation laws, as for instance the principle of energy conservation. The elementary particles obey some conservation laws valid and known in macrophysics, but there are also laws valid for them only. Finally, we shall see that the characteristic properties of elementary particles are of discrete, quantum nature.

B. Forces

The interaction of elementary particles is now considered to be governed by four types of forces, or, briefly said, there are four types of interactions. Two of them have been known for a long time in classical physics — gravitational and electromagnetic forces. In studying the atomic nucleus, two more forces were discovered. A strong nuclear force, which can overcome repulsive electric force between protons, is responsible for the binding of nucleons into nuclei. Another kind of force is responsible for such transformations as beta decay. It is considerably weaker than the strong nuclear force. Hence, they are usually named "strong" and "weak" interaction, respectively. It is not known yet whether the four known interactions — gravitational, electromagnetic, strong, and weak — are connected more intimately at a deeper level. So far, such connection is believed to have been found only between electro-magnetic and weak interactions.

Precise expressions for the gravitational and the electromagnetic interactions have been found. It was Newton that formulated the gravitation law, which, we recall, states that the force E∫ between two bodies of masses m_1 and m_2, which are a distance r apart, is

$$F_g = C_g \, m_1 \, m_2 / r^2 \tag{1}$$

where C∫ is a constant which depends on the system of units used. The electric force between charged bodies can be expressed in the same form (Coulomb's law), with masses replaced by electric charges, and the constant C is, of course, different. Such simple expressions have not been found for nuclear interactions, so that approximate models have to be used.

Of special interest for our further considerations are two characteristics of interactions: (1) the *strength*, and (2) their dependence on distance, or *range*. Both are quantitatively given in the force laws. It can be seen from (1) that the gravitational and electromagnetic forces decrease with increasing distance. The ranges of these forces are in principle infinite. This is illustrated, for example, by the mutual attraction of celestial bodies. The strength of both nuclear forces decreases much more rapidly with distance. The effective range of strong interactions is of the order of 10^{-15}m, while that of weak interactions is substantially smaller.

From expression (1) and the equivalent one for the electric force it can be calculated that for the same distance, the gravitational force between the two protons is weaker than the electric force by a factor of 10^{36}. The relative strengths of all four types of interactions, together with their ranges are given in Table 4.

The following conclusions can be drawn from Table 4:

- In the presence of any of the three other interactions, gravitation can be completely neglected. All theoretical treatment of nuclear experiments, including the radioactive decay, are done without taking into account the gravitational force.
- The nuclear forces are confined to the nucleus. If we imagine two atoms "touching" each other, they interact only electromagnetically, while the two nuclei do not feel their mutual nuclear fields.
- The nucleus is very small and strongly bound, while the electron cloud covers relatively much larger space and is less strongly bound. That allows separate approaches to nuclear and electron cloud phenomena, which simplifies the treatment.

The elementary particles are not all involved in all four interactions:

- Nucleons are involved in all four types of interaction.
- Electrons do not feel the strong nuclear force and participate in the other three interactions.
- Photons do not participate in strong and weak interaction. They play an essential role in electromagnetic interaction, while Einstein found that they feel the gravitational field too.
- Neutrinos participate only in weak and gravitational interactions. Since they are not charged and their mass is found to be very close to zero, their interaction with matter is extremely weak. Special, very large detectors and strong sources are needed to detect neutrinos.

C. Electrons, Photons, and Electromagnetic Interactions

The first elementary particle to be discovered, by the end of last century, was the electron. Two basic properties of elementary particles were revealed. First, the *identity* — all electrons

Table 4
THE RELATIVE STRENGTH AND THE RANGE OF INTERACTIONS

Type of interaction	Strong	Electromagnetic	Weak	Gravitational
Example of process or system where it is of importance	Binding of nucleons into nuclei	Gamma decay Binding of electrons to nuclei	Beta decay	Solar system
Relative strength	1	10^{-2}	10^{-13}	10^{-38}
Range, m	10^{-15}	Infinite	Less than 10^{-15}	Infinite

have the same charge. Second, their charge is the smallest possible, representing the unit of charge, all other amounts of electricity encountered in nature being integer multiples of the electron charge. The *elementary quantum of electricity* carried by the electron is

$$e = 1.6 \times 10^{-20} \text{ (electromagnetic units)}$$

$$= 1.6 \times 10^{-19} \text{ Coulombs} \qquad (2)$$

The elementary charge can be negative and positive. The positive electron is produced or annihilated always in pair with a negative electron. To produce an electron-positron pair it is necessary to expend an energy equivalent to the double rest mass of the electron, that is, $2 m_0 c^2 = 1.02$ MeV. A photon with energy greater than 1.02 MeV can produce an electron-positron pair. For this, the presence of charged particle is needed, so that the total energy and momentum are conserved. Conversely, when a positron and electron are annihilated, an energy of 1.02 MeV is released. This energy must be shared between two photons, so that momentum is conserved. This means that whenever we deal with positron sources, such as, for instance, the radioactive beta source emitting positive electrons, it will also produce photons with energy of a half of MeV.

The electron is a stable particle. It cannot disappear in a collision with another electron. In a collision with a nucleus, the probability that an electron will induce a reaction in which it will disappear is also negligible. Another possible disappearance — the annihilation with a positron — is negligible, since positrons seldom appear in nature. When electrons pass through matter their energy is absorbed, but the electrons themselves are practically not. When an electron loses all of its energy, it remains in the medium in which it is stopped.

In describing neutrino and antineutrino, we have already mentioned that, from the viewpoint of classical physics, they seem to rotate in opposite directions. All elementary particles possess this property of rotation called *spin*. It is, however, a quantum property. Each kind of elementary particle can have an integer or half integer number of units of spin, the unit being Planck's constant $\hbar = h/2\pi = 1.05 \times 10^{-34}$ joule/sec. All electrons have a spin of $1/2\hbar$.

The mass of an electron at rest, which never happens, is

$$m_0 = 9.1 \times 10^{-31} \text{ kg} \qquad (3)$$

The electron mass increases with energy according to a law from Einstein's special relativity, and is about $2m_0$ at an energy of 0.5 MeV, $3m_0$ at 1 MeV, $10\ m_0$ at 5 MeV, and $2000\ m_0$ at 1000 MeV.

The energy equivalent of the electron rest mass is

$$m_0 c^2 = 0.511 \text{ MeV} \qquad (4)$$

The electrons are very fast particles, so that already at low energies their velocities are very high. An electron with energy as low as 1 eV has a speed of nearly 600 km/sec, while at 18 keV it rises to one fourth of the velocity of light.

1. Photons and Electromagnetic Interaction

The concept of photon was introduced by Einstein to explain a newly discovered phenomenon called photoelectric effect, which could not be interpreted by classical theory of electromagnetic waves. He showed that at higher energies the electromagnetic radiation can be presented as a beam of energy quanta, or more simply said, energy packets, called photons. Every photon has an energy E, which is the product of the frequency of electromagnetic radiation ν and Planck's constant $\hbar$

$$E = h\nu \tag{5}$$

The velocity of the photon has to be equal to velocity of light, and then its mass has to be zero. Its momentum p is

$$p = E/c = h\nu/c = h/\lambda \tag{6}$$

These two formulae connect the wave characteristics ν and λ with corpuscular ones p and E. Hence, electromagnetic radiation can behave both as a wave and as a particle.

An isolated photon is stable. Alone, without the presence of another charged particle, it cannot undergo transformation, since conservation laws would be violated.

The photons play an important role in the theoretical explanation of the *electromagnetic interaction*. It is considered that two electric charges interact by emission and absorption of virtual photons. An electron emits for instance such a photon which is absorbed by another electron. The time lapse between emission and absorption is so short that, according to the Heisenberg uncertainty principle, it is not sufficient for a measurement of a photon. Therefore, such a photon is said to be *virtual*. The Heisenberg uncertainty principle connects the time of measurement Δt, with the uncertainty in the energy measured in this time interval ΔE, by the relation

$$\Delta E \, \Delta t \approx \hbar \tag{7}$$

Since Planck's constant $\hbar$ is very small, there are values of Δt for which the uncertainty ΔE in the measurement of energy is larger than the photon energy ΔE itself, which means that such an energy cannot be measured. The virtual photons remain undetected but their effects are real and seen as the action of one charged particle at another. The highly theoretical concept of virtual particles represent the present day answer to the old challenging problem of the action at distance.

A characteristic of a virtual process is that each of its stages taken separately may not obey the energy conservation laws, but the laws are satisfied by the process when taken as a whole. A free electron can neither emit nor absorb a real photon, since in this case the laws of conservation of energy and momentum would not be satisfied simultaneously. When another charged particle is near, to share momentum and energy, the emission and absorption become possible.

D. Nucleons and Nuclear Forces
1. Nucleons
Nuclear processes can be described by assuming that atomic nuclei are made up of protons and neutrons. These are called by the common name *nucleons*, not only because they are

the only constituents of nuclei, but also because they have many properties in common. Their masses and sizes are similar, they can transform into each other, and, apart from proton charge effect, they behave in the same way in the nucleus. They differ from each other by the fact that the proton is charged, whereas the neutron is not, and by their stability. A proton in free state is a stable particle, while the neutron is radioactive and transforms by beta decay into a proton, emitting also an electron and an antineutrino (half-life equal to 11.3 min).

Masses of the nucleons are

$$\text{proton mass} \;=\; m_p \;=\; 1.67243 \times 10^{-27}\,\text{kg} \qquad (8)$$

$$\text{neutron mass} \;=\; m_n \;=\; 1.67474 \times 10^{-27}\,\text{kg} \qquad (9)$$

As we can see, the masses of the nucleons are very small, and approximately the same, the neutron being heavier by 0.14%.

The energies which must be expended for the production of nucleons are

$$\text{energy equivalent of proton rest mass} \;=\; 938.2\,\text{MeV} \qquad (10)$$

$$\text{energy equivalent of neutron rest mass} \;=\; 939.5\,\text{MeV} \qquad (11)$$

2. Nuclear Forces

The model for description of nuclear forces is similar to the model of electrical force. In analogy with electrons which exchange virtual photons, nucleons are considered to exchange virtual mesons. There are several kinds of mesons with various masses. The lightest ones, called pions, are most abundantly produced in virtual processes, and we can confine our considerations to their role.

Since three types of pions, the positive, the negative, and the neutral, have been found experimentally, several modes of their emission and absorption are possible. A neutron, for instance, can undergo a transformation during a very short time into a proton and a negative pion. If the negative pion encounters another proton, it may be captured by the latter, so that a neutron is obtained, whereas the original neutron, which was involved in the virtual process, subsists as a proton. The total effect of this process is a charge exchange between a neutron and a proton, and there is also a binding action. Charged pions are exchanged by a proton and a neutron, whereas neutral pions are exchanged between two protons and between two neutrons. These virtual pion exchanges describe the attraction between the nucleons.

There is an important difference in virtual "behavior" between photons and pions, due to their masses. While photon has zero mass, the mass of the negative pion, expressed in energy units, is 140 MeV. The Heisenberg relation limits the duration of the virtual process, for such a heavy particle, to 4.7×10^{-24} sec. In such a short time a pion, even if it moved with the velocity of light, could not travel a distance larger than 1.4×10^{-15}m. Two nucleons can interact only if they are within that range. This explains why nuclear interaction has a very short range compared to electromagnetic interactions.

The size of nucleons is determined by the size of cloud of virtual mesons in the similar way to the dimensions of atom being determined by the size of its electron cloud. It follows that the radius of a nucleon is smaller than 1.4×10^{-15}m, and also they must be closely packed in the nucleus, in order to interact.

3. Atomic Nuclei

The atomic nucleus is a system of nucleons whose binding depends on the strong nuclear attractive force, and a hundred times weaker repulsive electric force acting between protons. Nuclear forces differ from electric forces not only in strength but also in range. Since the electric forces are of infinite range, each proton in a nucleus is acted upon by the repulsive forces of all the others. The number of bonds between pairs of protons is equal to

$$Z(Z-1)/2 \qquad Z = \text{number of protons} \qquad (12)$$

It shows that the repulsion between protons in a nucleus increases with the square of their number.

The nuclear attraction presents a different picture, because one nucleon can interact only with those that are "touching" it. If, let us say, a neutron is added to a medium-sized nucleus, most nucleons in the nucleus will not be influenced by this event, and will not be more tightly bound because of its presence. The nuclear attraction is approximately proportional to the number of nucleons in the nucleus. All this means that as the nucleus increases in size, the electric repulsion increases more rapidly than the nuclear attraction. Since nuclear interactions are much stronger, light and medium nuclei are very stable. In heavier nuclei, stability is achieved by a relative increase of the number of neutrons, so that it exceeds the number of protons. However, nothing can stabilize nuclei above bismuth.

a. Mass and Binding Energy

The mass of a nucleus is approximately equal to the nucleon mass multiplied by their number, A. The sum of masses of the constituent nucleons is about 0.85% larger than the mass of the nucleus. The free nucleons give up a small part of their masses when they form a tightly bound nucleus. The lost mass, ΔM, is transformed to energy, which is released when nucleus is formed. The total released energy, called *binding energy* of the nucleus, B, is equal

$$B = \Delta Mc^2 \qquad (13)$$

where c is the velocity of light.

The binding energy is an indication of stability, and its proper measure is the *mean binding energy per nucleon* f

$$f = B/A \qquad (14)$$

The value of f is known with high precision for each nuclide. It is given for large number of different nuclides in the graph in Figure 2. Several conclusions can be drawn from an inspection of the graph:

• The mean binding energy per nucleon f is approximately constant, varying within a narrow energy interval from 7.4 to 8.8 MeV, for almost all nuclides. The approximate constancy of f indicates that the nuclear binding force is nearly proportional to the number of nucleons A.
• An average value of f, which can be used for rough estimations is

$$f = 8 \text{ MeV} \qquad (15)$$

• There is a decrease of f for heavy nuclei, which is accounted for by an increase in the repulsion between their protons.

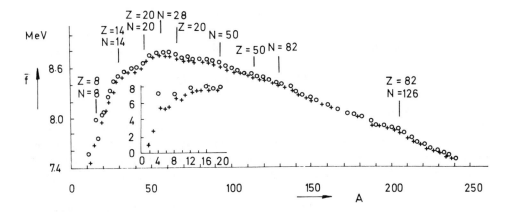

FIGURE 2. The mean binding energy per nuclear f shown as a function of A. Even-even nuclei are shown by circles, and odd nuclei by crosses. The light nuclei are shown in the insert with expanded A scale.

- For light nuclei, f also decreases, since in such nuclei the major part of nucleons are at a surface of the nucleus, where they are not as tightly bound as those in the interior.
- A closer inspection of the graph reveals local variations. The most important of them are differences between even-even nuclei shown by circles, and odd nuclei shown by crosses. The values of f for even-even nuclei are always higher than those of nearby odd nuclei. There are, in addition, other small local variation of f, which shall turn out to be important when we consider the beta decay.

b. Size

All nuclei have approximately the same density, so that the volume of nucleus linearly increases with the number of nucleons A. Most nuclei are of spherical shape. In some portions of the periodic table, such as rare earths, nuclei are deformed and have ellipsoidal form. Since the deformation is not considerable, one can roughly assume that all nuclei are spherical and speak of their radius. If A nucleons can be packed into a sphere, its radius R will be proportional to $A^{1/3}$. The numerical value of the radius of the nucleus has been experimentally established to be

$$R = 1.07 \times 10^{-15} A \text{ m} \tag{16}$$

It follows from this formula that the radius of even the heaviest nuclei does not exceed 10^{-14}m.

When speaking of the radius, we have to bear in mind that boundary of the nucleus is not sharp, since its density progressively decreases towards its surface. It is a dynamic surface formed by nucleons rapidly circulating.

c. Spin

Nucleons perform two kinds of rotational motions in the nucleus, which have a very distant analogy with the solar system. Each rotates around its own axis, and is at the same time orbiting in the nucleus itself. The intrinsic angular momentum or spin of every nucleon is equal to $\pm \hbar/2$, while the orbiting angular momenta can be only integer multiples of $\hbar$. The nucleon movements are so ordered and coordinated, that the sum of angular moments projected on an axis, called nuclear spin, is relatively small. The simplest is the case of even-even nuclei, which all have in the ground state their spin equal to zero. The ground state spins of odd-even nuclei are half-integers (1/2, 3/2, 5/2 $\hbar$ . . .), and odd-odd nuclei have the integer values (1,2,3,4 $\hbar$ . . .).

The spin of excited states differ from ground state by an integer value of $\hbar$, usually small multiples. All nuclear transitions are sensitive to the spin difference between the initial and final state, the probability of transition decreasing with the increase of the spin change.

III. NUCLEAR INSTABILITIES AND DECAYS

A. Nuclear Instabilities

We have seen that there are 265 stable nuclides in nature. If we produce an artificial nucleus, by injecting one or more nucleons into a stable one, the new nucleus is always, without exception, unstable. The artificial nucleus decays, sooner or later, by one of the available modes of decay. Why do these artificially produced nuclei decay? What are the conditions for nuclear instability?

Using mathematical terminology, the conditions for nuclear instability can be divided into two categories — necessary and sufficient ones.

The energy condition is a necessary one. A nuclear decay is a spontaneous process, which can occur only if energy is released, and the nucleus passes from a higher energy level to a lower one. In the process of radioactive decay the binding energy of the nucleus is increased, and the energy difference between the initial and final state of the nucleus is partly used to produce the transformation and partly is transferred to the emitted particles. It can also be said that in the decay the total mass of the system decreases, to account for the released energy.

There are three basic types of nuclear instability:

1. Dynamic instability, which refers, among other things, to alpha decay and to fission processes
2. Beta instability
3. Gamma instability

The energy condition is manifested in the critical dependence of all the three types of instability on the energy released in the decay. The decay probability sharply increases with the released energy.

The energy condition is a necessary, but not sufficient one. Every change of any physical system is regulated by forces and conservation laws, and also depends on the structure of the system. The larger the change of structure, the smaller is the probability of transition. In nuclear systems the structure indicator is the nuclear spin, the larger spin change corresponding to slower transition. A simple example of the role that forces are playing, is the alpha decay, where we shall see that a kind of barrier is built by protons, preventing alpha particle to leave the nucleus. Finally, some conservation laws are quite universal, while some of them are specific for elementary particles. Before considering the decay modes, we should briefly review the conservation laws.

1. Conservation Laws

1. Mass-energy conservation. The sum of mass and energy remains unchanged in nuclear transitions. We should bear in mind that energy may take the form of kinetic energy, or of internal energy which particles may possess within bound systems.
2. Linear momentum conservation. The linear momenta are vector quantities, the sum of which remains unchanged in any transformation of an isolated system.
3. Angular momentum conservation. This represents the conservation of rotational motions. The spin of the nucleus before decay is equal to the sum of the nuclear spin after the decay and the angular momentum of emitted particles.

4.   Charge conservation. The total charge remains unchanged in the decay, and may only be redistributed between the products of the decay. It follows from this law that electrons can be produced or annihilated only in pairs, together with positrons. This is one of the laws which, by virtue of the stability of electron, ensures the stability of matter. It forbids the electron to decay into a particle having a mass smaller than its own, which is electrically neutral, that is, into neutrino.

5.   Electron family (lepton) conservation. Radioactive beta decay gives an electron and a neutrino, which together make a lepton family. If the particles, that is, the electron and the neutrino, are assigned the number $+1$, and their antiparticles, that is, the positron and the antineutrino are assigned the number -1, the sum of these numbers is conserved in the decay. It means that one of them has to be a particle, and another antiparticle.

6.   Heavy particle (barion) conservation. The proton and the neutron are the lightest particles in the barion family. As in the case of electron, they can be assigned the number $+1$, and the antiproton and antineutron the number -1. The sum of these numbers remains unchanged in the decay. This law forbids nucleons to decay into particles of smaller mass, such as mesons. Thus nuclear stability is ensured.

2. Dynamic Instability

A nucleus is considered to be dynamically unstable if there exist prevalent conditions for its splitting into two or more fragments. Since the probability of such a decay sharply decreases with an increasing number of fragments, we shall dwell only on decay into two fragments.

The necessary energy condition for a nucleus to split into two fragments is that these fragments be more stable than the original nucleus, that is, that these have a smaller total mass, and that the mass difference strengthens their individual binding and appears as energy released in the decay. When the energy condition is mathematically formulated, by using the simplest model, it turns out that the elements above $Z = 40$, that is, the entire heavier half of the periodic table should be unstable. Thus, the world would be depleted and reduced to about 40 elements only, if the energy condition, formulated in such a way, were also the sufficient one. Of course, it is not, because it takes into account only the initial and final states but not the dynamics of splitting into two fragments. During the splitting the nucleus undergoes continuous deformations, as seen in Figure 3. It must stretch out, then become narrower at a certain place, and finally split. This process is counteracted by the forces in the nucleus, against which a certain work has to be done, which requires a definite energy. When this energy requirement is compared with the energy released in the splitting, it usually turns out that the necessary energy is larger than the energy available to the nucleus. Then, according to classical physics, no splitting could occur, whereas quantum mechanics allows a final probability for the splitting, provided the difference in energy is not too great.

Two most important kinds of dynamic instability are the fission and the alpha decay. In the second case instead of speaking of the splitting of the nucleus, one usually speaks of the alpha-particle escaping the nucleus. The energy situation can be characterized as a barrier hindering the escape of an alpha-particle. However, the alpha-particle, after many attempts, may succeed in escaping from the nucleus, as if it leaked through a tunnel.

The probability of leakage of an alpha-particle through a tunnel is greater, the shorter the tunnel and the lower barrier. For most alpha decays, an energy exceeding 4 MeV is necessary for the alpha particle to leak through tunnel.

3. Beta Instability

In this case the number of nucleons in the nucleus remains unchanged, but the proton to

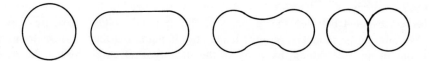

FIGURE 3.   The splitting of a nucleus.

neutron ratio is changed by the transformation of a proton into a neutron and vice versa. The transformation involves two more particles, an electron and a neutrino. The processes of beta decay can be written as follows:

$$n \rightarrow p + e^- + \bar{\nu} \qquad \text{negative electron emission} \qquad (17)$$

$$p \rightarrow n + e^+ + \nu \qquad \text{positron emission} \qquad (18)$$

$$p + e^- \rightarrow n + \nu \qquad \text{electron capture} \qquad (19)$$

Instead of emitting a positron, a proton can capture an electron from the K shell and transform into a neutron by the emission of a neutrino.

Four conservation laws are satisfied in the above processes: mass-energy, charge, barion number, and lepton number conservation.

Since there is no barrier for an electron leaving the nucleus, the energy condition for beta instability is a sufficient one, with, however, always present the structure effect expressed by an attenuation increasing with the spin change.

In this case the energy effect is reduced to the mass difference between the neighboring isobars. If the atom with higher Z has a smaller mass, a β^- decay takes place. In the opposite case, when the atom with higher Z has a larger mass, an electron capture takes place, if the mass difference is larger than the binding energy of the electron to be captured, while for positron emission the mass difference must be larger than the double electron rest mass. For this reason no two stable isobars can exist, and they form a decay chain, as illustrated in Figure 4.

4. Gamma Instability

In the gamma decay the composition of the nucleus remains the same, and only its energy state changes. By the emission of a photon, the nucleus passes from a higher to a lower energy state. Such a decay usually follows alpha decay and especially beta decay, as well as a number of reactions, since they all often lead the nucleus not to the ground, but to an excited state.

A photon can readily escape from the nucleus. Thus, for gamma decay the energy condition is not only a necessary but also a sufficient one. Instead of the emission of a photon, the excitation energy can be transferred to an electron from one of the shells, a process known as *internal conversion*. When the excitation energy is larger than 1 MeV, an electron pair can be also produced.

B. Alpha Decay

The alpha-particle is the nucleus of the helium atom and represents a very stable combination of two protons and two neutrons. It is not a permanent constituent of the nucleus, but rather a transient system, which can be formed, exists for a certain time, and then dissolves. In heavier nuclides, there are alpha radioactive nuclei, in which sooner or later, an alpha-particle manages to leak through the barrier.

27

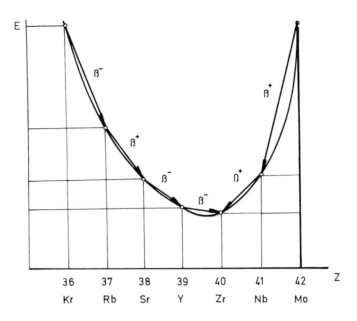

FIGURE 4.   The decay chain of isobars with nucleon number A = 90.

1. Energies and Half-Lives

There are two outstanding characteristics of alpha decay. First, the energy range is relatively narrow for a given element. Most of the alpha-particle energies fall within the interval of 4 to 7 MeV. Lower alpha-particle energies are rather infrequent, but may be as low as 2 MeV for lighter elements, where the barrier is smaller. In a few special cases, an alpha-particle energy of 10 MeV is encountered.

The second important characteristic of alpha decay is a critical dependence of half-life on the energy. It is illustrated in Figure 5, which shows the correlation between the half-lives $T_{1/2}$ and energies of alpha emitters in the thorium family, which is one of the natural radioactive series. The half-life of Th-232, which emits alpha-particles of an energy of 4 MeV is 1.4×10^{10} years. At the other end, the energy is roughly doubled, being 8.78 MeV for Po-212, but the half-life has decreased to 10^{-14} years.

It should be noted that the decay energy is shared between the alpha-particle and the nucleus, which in the emission process, recoils in the direction opposite to that of the flight of the alpha-particle. Since the masses of the alpha radioactive nuclei are about 50 times larger than the mass of the alpha-particle, only about 2% of the total decay energy is carried off by the recoiling nucleus.

2. Alpha Spectra

The energy spectrum may contain 1 to 20 lines corresponding to transitions usually from the ground state of the parent nucleus to the excited states and the ground state of the product nucleus. The transition probability depends critically on the energy and also on the spin change.

In the transitions between two even-even nuclei, which always have the spin of ground state equal to zero, the transition between two ground states is by far the most abundant, since the spin change is zero and the available energy the largest. An example of such a spectrum is shown in Figure 6. It can be seen that for every four decays, three of them take place between the ground states.

The transitions between odd nuclei are more complex and due to the influence of the spin change, the most probable transition does not necessarily lead to the ground state.

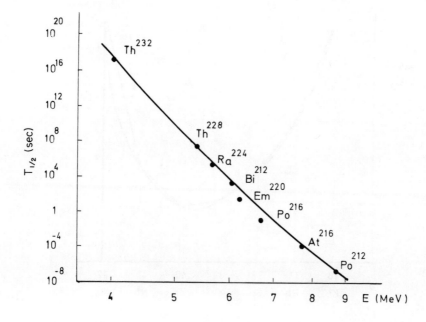

FIGURE 5.   The correlation between the half-lives $T_{1/2}$ and energies E in the thorium family.

The alpha transitions to the excited states are followed by the gamma decay. In the even-even nuclei the transition to the first excited state is usually much more probable than to higher states, so that the gamma transition between the first excited state and the ground state is the most prominent in the gamma-spectrum. For odd nuclei the gamma spectrum is usually more complex.

3. Origin

The earliest known alpha emitters belonged to the naturally radioactive uranium, thorium, and actinium families. All three families together contain about 30 alpha emitters. Subsequently many other alpha emitters have been artificially produced. In the region between uranium and bismuth another hundred alpha emitters were produced.

Another important group is made up of 15 artificially produced elements heavier than uranium, where there are nearly 100 alpha emitters.

A third, smallest group consist of alpha emitters in the rare earth region, with energies between 2 to 4 MeV, and correspondingly long half-lives.

4. Alpha Sources

During the first four decades of this century use was made chiefly of naturally radioactive alpha emitters, especially Po-212. Presently, artificial ones are more often used, especially transuraniums. Table 5 gives the basic characteristics of some alpha emitters used in practice.

C. Nuclear Fission

We have seen that very heavy nuclei are increasingly unstable due to electrostatic repulsion between protons. An alpha-particle can detach itself from the nucleus already in the rare earth region and beginning with thorium, all heavier elements have isotopes which can spontaneously split into two, usually unequal parts. There are known now about 60 nuclides undergoing a spontaneous fission. We reproduce in Table 6 a selection of these nuclides.

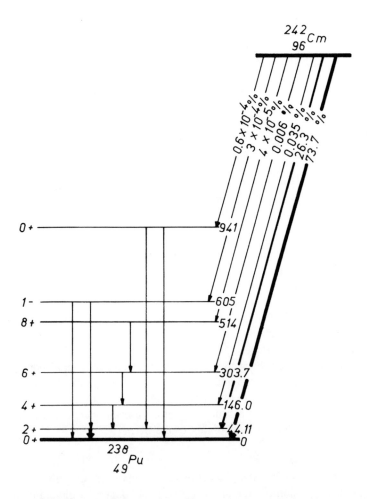

FIGURE 6.   The decay scheme of ^{242}Cm, with seven alpha transitions to ground and excited states of ^{238}Pu.

Table 5
THE BASIC CHARACTERISTICS OF SOME OFTEN USED
α EMITTERS

Nucleus	Half-life	Mode of production	Prominent lines in the spectrum	
			α(MeV)	γ(MeV)
^{210}Po	138 days	Decay ^{210}Bi(RaE) ^{209}Bi(n,γ)^{210}Bi $\xrightarrow{\beta}$^{210}Po	5.305(100%) 4.5 (10^{-3}%)	0.8
^{239}Pu	24,410 years	^{238}U(n,γ)^{239} U$\xrightarrow{\beta}$Np ^{239}Np $\xrightarrow{\beta}$^{239}Pu	5.147(72%) 5.134(17%) 5.09 (11%)	0.052
^{238}Pu	89 years	^{237}Np(n,γ)^{238}Np $\xrightarrow{^-\beta}$Pu	5.495(72%) 5.452(28%)	0.043
^{242}Cm	162 days	^{239}Pu(n,γ)→. . .^{242}Cm	6.11 (74%) 6.07 (26%)	0.044
^{244}Cm	18 years	^{242}Pu(n,γ)→. . .^{244}Cm	5.80 (77%) 5.76 (23%)	0.043

Table 6
THE HALF-LIFE FOR SPONTANEOUS
FISSION OF SOME SELECTED NUCLIDES

Nuclide	Half-life	Nuclide	Half-life
^{232}Th	1×10^{21} years	^{250}Cf	1.7×10^4 sec
^{235}U	3.5×10^{17} years	^{254}Cf	5.2×10^6 sec
^{238}U	8.2×10^{15} years	^{256}Cf	7.4×10^2 sec
^{239}Pu	5.5×10^{15} years	^{254}Fm	2.0×10^4 sec
^{240}Pu	1.3×10^{11} years	^{256}Fm	1.2×10^4 sec
^{242}Pu	6.8×10^{10} years	^{258}Fm	4.1×10^{-4} sec
^{242}Cm	6.1×10^6 years	^{258}No	1.2×10^{-3} sec
^{250}Cm	1.1×10^4 years		

An inspection of the Table 6 shows two kinds of regularities:

1. The half-life for spontaneous fission decreases for heavier elements. The probability of fission is very roughly proportional to Z^2/A.
2. The probability of spontaneous fission is much larger for an even-even nucleus than for the nearby odd nuclei.

While the first effect seems to be accounted for by the electrostatic repulsive forces between the protons, the second indicates the importance of nuclear structure. When changing from a given structure of initial nucleus to two new structures, it seems easier to dispose of pairs of nucleons, than single ones. The restructuring of even-even nucleus requires less energy, and therefore more is left for the overcoming of the barrier.

1. Neutron Induced Fission
For practical purposes, such as the production of radionuclides, the only important process is the neutron induced fission of uranium, and to a lesser degree of plutonium and thorium. We see from the Table 6 that the half-life for a spontaneous fission of U-235 is very long. When a neutron enters into a U-235 nucleus, a new nucleus is produced with a different structure, which depends on received energy. A part of the energy can be received from the kinetic energy of entering neutron itself, which in case of thermalized neutrons is very small. A much larger amount of energy is received from the binding of the neutron itself. In the case of U-235 this energy amounts to 6.5 MeV. It turns out that such an excitation energy is sufficient for overcoming the fission barrier.

In the case of U-238 the capture of a neutron changes an even-even nucleus into an odd-even one, which is less stable. The binding energy of such a neutron is only 4.8 MeV, which is not enough to overcome the barrier. It was found experimentally that for an appreciable fission rate, the neutrons should have an energy over 1.5 MeV, while at lower energies the probability of fission rapidly decreases.

For practical purposes, the use of U-235 as a source of energy is easier, because it can be split with neutrons of any energy.

2. Energy Liberated in Fission
We have seen that the stability of nuclides is greatest in the middle of the periodic table and decreases for heavy nuclides. It follows that in the case of fission, an unstable nucleus is breaking up into two much more stable nuclei. Since the difference in binding energy is about 1 MeV per nucleon, (see Figure 2) and there are more than 200 nucleons involved, the liberated energy should be over 200 MeV. It is about 100 times larger than the energy liberated in beta decays.

Table 7
THE ENERGIES LIBERATED
IN FISSION OF U-235 BY
THERMAL NEUTRONS

Carrier	Energy, MeV
Fragments	166
Free neutrons	5
Prompt gamma rays	8
Beta and gamma decays	24
	203

The energy liberated in fission is distributed between fission products in a complex way. Most of the energy is carried by two *fission fragments*. Each fission produces two to three *free neutrons* which take away a smaller amount of energy. A violent process such as fission necessarily gives off some energy during the structural rearrangements. It is emitted as electromagnetic energy and called *prompt gamma rays*. Finally, since the heavy nuclei have a large proportion of neutrons, the fission fragments have more neutrons than necessary for stability. Several beta decays, changing neutrons into protons, might be necessary to produce a stable nucleus. The energy liberated in these beta and gamma decay represents the final portion of the total liberated in fission.

As an example we shall give in Table 7 the energies liberated in the fission of U-235 by thermal neutrons.

The last item in Table 7 — beta and gamma decays — is of interest for the users of radioactive nuclides.

3. Fission Products

The protons and neutrons in the nuclei form shells in some way similar to electron shells around the nucleus. The shell formation contributes to the stability of the nucleus in such a way that closed shells are more stable than uncompleted ones. This is believed to be the main reason why the heavy nuclei do not split symmetrically. The most probable fission products of U-235 are around the mass numbers A = 35 and A = 139.

The fission products of U-235 cover the mass range from A = 72 to A = 161. There are about 100 ways in which the uranium nucleus can split. The direct fragments are radioactive with a very short half-life. Several (2 to 6) radioactive transformations are necessary before a stable nucleus is reached. The half-lives of these beta decays are usually increasing, although the local structure effects may sometimes reverse the trend for one of the series members.

All radioactive members of fission fragment series are called fission products. There are now known more than 360 radioactive isotopes in the families of fission products. Table 8 shows a few selected radioactive series produced in fission.

a. Fission Produced Radioactive Sources

The fission produced radioactive series that we have selected in Table 8, are those where last members are mostly used for practical purposes. The most important are ^{90}Sr-^{90}Y as pure beta-ray source, and ^{137}Cs as a convenient gamma-source.

D. Beta Decay

Four particles are involved in a beta decay: proton, neutron, electron, and neutrino. A proton changes into a neutron, or vice versa, and a pair of leptons — an electron and a

Table 8
THE EXAMPLES OF RADIOACTIVE SERIES PRODUCED IN FISSION

^{90}Br(1.9)$\rightarrow$^{90}Kr(33 sec)$\rightarrow$^{90}Rb(2.5 min)$\rightarrow$^{90}Sr(28.8 yr)$\rightarrow$^{90}Y(64 hr)$\rightarrow$^{90}Zr
^{137}I (24 sec)$\rightarrow$^{137}Xe(3.9 min)$\rightarrow$^{137}Cs(30 y)$\rightarrow$^{137}Ba
^{143}Xe(1 sec)$\rightarrow$^{137}Cs(2 sec)$\rightarrow$^{137}Ba(13 sec)$\rightarrow$^{137}La(14 min)$\rightarrow$^{137}Ce(33 hr)$\rightarrow$^{137}Pr(13.6 d)$\rightarrow$^{137}Nd
^{147}Ce(56 sec)$\rightarrow$^{147}Pr(13 min)$\rightarrow$^{147}Nd(11 d)$\rightarrow$^{147}Pm(2.62 yr)$\rightarrow$^{147}Sm(1 $\times$ 10^{11}y)$\rightarrow$^{143}Nd

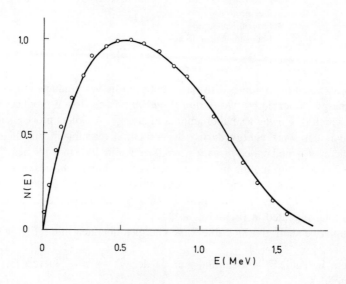

FIGURE 7.   The spectrum of ^{32}P.

neutrino — leave the nucleus. If a neutron transforms into proton, an electron always leaves the nucleus, while in the opposite change, instead of a positron leaving the nucleus, an orbital electron can be captured.

1. Beta Spectra

The electron and the neutrino share the available decay energy in a statistical way. Each of these can carry away any part of the available energy, from zero to a maximum, the other carrying the rest. The spectrum of electrons is, therefore, basically determined by statistics, but since other physical factors can influence the energy of outgoing electrons, beginning with the electric field produced by protons, the shape of the electron spectrum is not symmetrical. As an illustration the spectrum of ^{32}P is shown in Figure 7. One can see that the lower energy part of the spectrum is more abundant and the mean energy is about 0.3 E_{max}.

Beta emission often leads, not to one, but to several energy levels of the product nucleus. The relative probability of a transition is, very roughly speaking, directly proportional to the energy difference, and inversely proportional to the spin difference between the states of parent and product nucleus.

The positron spectrum is very similar to the negative electron spectrum, but is somewhat shifted towards higher energies. Since the nucleus repels the emitted positron, it thereby, increases more appreciably the energy of slower electrons. The mean energy of the positron spectrum is 0.4 E_{max}.

The maximum energies of continuous beta spectra are usually less than 2 to 3 MeV. In the case of some light elements, very high energies, up to 15 MeV, are encountered.

Table 9
THE BASIC CHARACTERISTICS OF SOME
FREQUENTLY USED BETA SOURCES

Source	Half-life	E_{max}, Mev	Production
^{3}H	12.33 years	0.186	^{9}B(d,2d),^{6}Li(n,γ)
^{14}C	5730 years	0.155	^{13}C(d,p),^{14}N(n,γ)
^{32}P	14.28 days	1.711	^{31}P(n,γ),^{32}S(n,γ)
^{45}Ca	165 days	0.258	^{44}Ca(n,γ)
^{90}Sr	28.8 years	0.546	Fission
^{90}Y	64 hr	2.28	Product of ^{90}Sr, fission

2. Electron Capture

This process competes with positron emission, especially for low transition energies and for high Z of the nucleus. In 90% of all cases the electron is captured from the K shell, which is closest to the nucleus. Hence, the term ''K capture'' is often used.

K capture produces a vacancy in the K shell. The filling of this vacancy by the emission of an X-ray or an Auger electron is the only detectable indication that the electron capture has occurred, since the emitted neutrino escape without interacting with the environment.

3. Beta Sources

The choice of a pure beta emitter for a definite purpose depends on various factors, such as the half-life, the energy, the mode of production, and the chemical properties. Table 9 gives the characteristics of several most frequently used beta sources.

E. Gamma Decay

Under gamma decay we understand an emission of a photon from an excited state of a nucleus to another lower energy state of the same nucleus, which can be either excited or ground state. Often a cascade of photons are emitted until ground state is reached.

The excited nuclear state can be obtained after the emission of a beta or alpha-particle, and also in the nuclear reactions. If we confine our attention to the radioactivity, then we should note that beta active isotopes are much more often used as sources of gamma radiation, because they are produced more easily and generally have a higher gamma radiation intensity than alpha emitters.

1. Energy Spectrum

The gamma spectrum is composed of lines. To every possible transition there is a corresponding definite photon energy. The degree to which the gamma spectrum is monokinetic can be judged by the fact that the energies of photons involved in the same transition may differ from each other by only $\Delta E = 10^{-3} - 10^{-10}$ eV. Since the gamma ray energy E is between $E = 10^4 - 10^6$ eV, it turns out that the relative differences in the photon energies for the same transitions are usually considerably less than $\Delta E/E \approx 10^{-7}$.

The lines of a gamma spectrum are of different intensities, which depend on the branching of the beta transitions and the relative probabilities of gamma transitions from the same nuclear energy level to various lower levels. (Figure 8).

The energies of gamma rays emitted by radioactive isotopes are usually lower than 2 to 3 MeV. In the case of some light nuclei, gamma ray energies of almost 10 MeV occur.

2. Half-Lives and Isomerism

The half-life of gamma decay is considerably shorter than that for alpha and beta decays

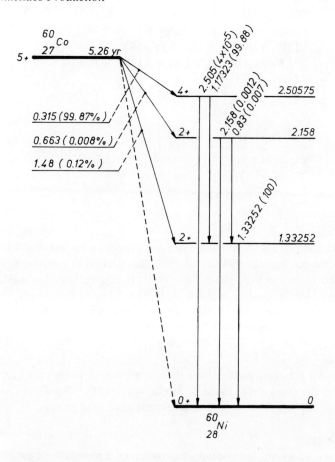

FIGURE 8.   The decay scheme of ^{60}Co. Two important gamma rays of
1.17 and 1.33 MeV are in cascade.

and is usually 10^{-6} to 10^{-13} sec. It is shorter for higher energy and smaller spin differences between the initial and final nuclear state.

In certain cases, when the spin difference is larger than 3 to 4 units, and energy of the transition is low, the half-life may be considerably longer, up to several years. Such transitions are called "isomeric".

3. Internal Conversion and Auger Effect

The emission of a photon is not the only process of nuclear deexcitation. A competing process is the ejection of an electron from one of the shells, to which the excitation energy has been transferred from the nucleus. The electron leaves the atom with an energy E_e equal to the gamma decay energy E_γ minus the electron binding energy E_B, which must be expanded for its liberation:

$$E_e = E_\gamma - E_B \tag{20}$$

Since the electron can be ejected from K, L, M, N . . . shells, which have different binding energies, several electron lines are obtained for each gamma transition E_γ. The probability of this process, called internal conversion, is highest for the K shell and decreases toward outer shells (Figure 9).

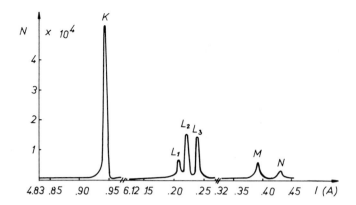

FIGURE 9. The internal conversion spectrum of 137 keV transition in
^{186}Re.

Internal conversion competes with photon emission, and, in a sense, these are two complementary processes. The probability of internal conversion increases with increasing Z and decreasing E, being negligible for light nuclei, but almost always occurring in heavy nuclei, especially at low transition energies.

In internal conversion and electron capture the involved electron leaves a vacancy in the shell that is soon filled by one of two competing processes. One is X-ray emission due to the transition of an electron from a more distant shell to a vacancy closer to the nucleus. The other is similar to internal conversion, but the energy difference due to the jump of the electron is not emitted as a photon. It is expended for the ejection of another electron from the same atom. If, let us say, the vacancy was in the K shell, and was filled with an electron from L shell, the energy obtained would suffice to eject an electron from the L shell or M shell. Thus, two vacancies appear instead of one. The Auger process may go on in more distant shells, increasing the number of vacancies. When the outermost shell is reached the atom may remain without up to, or more than five electrons. The overall process terminates in less than 10^{-9} sec. These Auger spectra appear as series of bunched electron lines at low energies. In the competition between the Auger process and X-ray emission, the former is more probable for light atoms while the latter is more probable for heavy atoms.

4. Photon Sources

The sources of photons can be divided in two classes according to the energy range and the origin of photons. The higher energy range includes gamma-ray sources from a few MeV down to 0.1 MeV. There is a large variety of these sources. Thus, one can choose, for almost any use, a source with suitable energy, half-life, intensity, and cost. Sources produced by an (N, γ) reaction in a nuclear reactor are most often used. Table 10 gives some of the characteristics of a number of such sources.

The sources of softer radiation are often the radioactive isotopes that decay by electron capture, which is followed by the emission of that X-radiation characteristic of the element produced by the decay. Table 11 gives the half-life of the radioactive nuclide and the energy of the most intense line in the spectrum (K, α') of some of these sources, which can be produced in a nuclear reactor.

F. Radioactive Decay

1. Physics of Exponential Laws

For two millenia, the scientists used only linear proportions in their attempts to describe

Table 10
THE BASIC CHARACTERISTICS OF
SOME FREQUENTLY USED γ-RAY
SOURCES. (ALL PRODUCED BY (n,γ)
REACTION)

Source	Half-life	E, MeV
^{24}Na	15 hr	2.7 and 1.3
^{72}Ga	14 hr	0.8(0.6-2.5)
^{140}La	40 hr	1.6(0.3-2.5)
^{110}Ag	252 days	0.6(0.1-1.5)
^{152}Eu, ^{154}Eu	13 years, 16 years	0.12(0.12-1.4)
^{60}Co	5.27 years	1.17 and 1.33
^{182}Ta	155 days	0.06-1.2
^{187}W	23.8 hr	0.07-0.8
^{192}Ir	74 days	0.3-0.6

Table 11
THE RADIONUCLIDES
USED AS SOURCES OF X
RAYS. ONLY THE
ENERGY OF MOST
PROMINENT (K,α') LINE
IS GIVEN (ALL
PRODUCED BY (n,γ)
REACTION)

Source	Half-life	E(k,α')keV
^{55}Fe	2.6 years	5.9
^{65}Zn	244 days	8.05
^{75}Se	118 days	10.05
^{170}Tm	128 days	52.4
^{204}Tl	3.7 years	70.8

the processes in nature. Since most of such processes are not linear, and could be reduced to them only in the infinitesimal range, the exact laws found can be numbered by the fingers on one hand. The breakthrough was made by experiments of Galileo, who discovered a physical law requiring a quadratic function, opening thereby the door for other mathematical functions. A few decades later, in the 17th century, Fermat and Pascal started developing the laws of chances. When in the next century Euler introduced the symbol e, and Poisson and Gauss developed their functions for distributions of chance events, the mathematical apparatus was ready in the 19th century for handling many natural phenomena that have several things in common:

1. The number of unit systems is large
2. All systems are identical
3. The systems are mutually independent
4. The same event can happen in any of them
5. The probability that an event shall happen in a time interval is independent of time elapsed, or the "age" of the system

These conditions are strictly met in atomic and nuclear physics where one deals with *large number* of *independent, identical* systems. The *identical* processes can happen in any one of them with a probability which is *independent of the "age" of systems*.

The typical systems are the particle beams in the accelerators, the targets, and the radioactive sources produced by interaction of beams and targets. Some of the requirements may be relaxed, as is the case of nuclear reactors, where the beam dissolves into 4π diffusion, and its energy spreads over a wide range. In more complex organic systems, including man and society, the parameter of identity is diffused into similarity, and the probability of the event is not uniquely determined. The law is then only approximately exponential.

A collection of a large number of such systems can be studied in two ways: (1) differentially, one examines how many systems undergo change in the unit of time, which is small compared to the change of the total number of systems. We find that the number of changes cannot be exactly predicted, being regulated by statistical laws, and we produce the probable distributions of changes. (2) From an integral point of view, we examine how the collection of systems change in time, and get exponential laws.

We shall consider first the exponential laws and leave statistics for the next chapter.

When we have a large number of systems N, and the probability of the event is independent on the age of a given system, then the number of events in unit time dN is proportional to the number of systems N. Simply, more systems will have more changes, and therefore

$$dN \sim N \tag{21}$$

In order to get an equation we have to include the probability of event for a system in unit time λ, which acts as a proportionality factor, so that we obtain

$$dN = \lambda \, Ndt \tag{22}$$

where dt denotes a relatively small unit of time.

There are always two complementary aspects in the change of a large number of systems. We can be interested in how the initial systems decrease or how the new ones are formed. Mathematically, it means that we shall have to put the sign minus in front of dN in the first case and sign plus for the second case.

$$\pm \, dN = \lambda \, Ndt \tag{23}$$

Since λ is constant, the solution of this differential equation is

$$N = N_0 \, e^{(\pm)\lambda t} \tag{24}$$

where N_0 is the initial number of considered systems, and N their number after a time t.

2. Activity

The law of decay (24) involves the number of radioactive atoms N_0 and N, which cannot be directly measured. We can measure the number of atoms decayed and we normalize them by introducing the concept of activity A, defined as number of decays per unit time. The activity is then given by the number of atoms initially present N, multiplied by the decay constant λ

$$A = N\lambda \tag{25}$$

Since λ is a constant, we obtain, when we multiply the Equation 25 by λ, and use (24)

$$A = A_0 \, e^{-\lambda t} \tag{26}$$

Thus we obtain the evolution in time of a statistically measured magnitude A.

3. Half-Life

Instead of the decay constant λ, it is more convenient to use the half-life $T^{1/2}$, which is defined as the time in which the activity is reduced by one half. The relation between λ and $T^{1/2}$ is obtained by the following calculation

$$A = A_0/2 = A_0 \exp(-\lambda \, T_{1/2})$$

$$1/2 = \exp(-\lambda \, T_{1/2})$$

$$\lambda \, T_{1/2} = \ln 2$$

$$T_{1/2} = 0.693/\lambda \tag{27}$$

4. Radioactive Series

We shall briefly consider only the case of a family of two members, because it is most important in practice. Moreover, once the mathematical treatment of two members is understood, it is easily extended to series with more members.

Let radioactive substance 1, which we call the parent, decay into radioactive substance 2, which we call the daughter, and let substance 2 decay into stable substance 3. Substance 1 decays with decay constant λ_1 to give substance 2, which itself immediately begins to decay with decay constant λ_2. While the number of decays of the first substance is given by simple decay law (24), for the second substance it is given by

$$N_2 = \lambda_1/(\lambda_2 - \lambda_1) \; N_1^0 \, [\exp(-\lambda_1 t) - \exp(-\lambda_2 t)] \tag{28}$$

where N_1^0 and $N_2^0 = 0$ are the number of atoms of two substances at $t = 0$, and N_2 is the number of atoms of substance 2 at time t.

The decay rate of the daughter depends on the ratio of the half-life of the parent to that of the daughter. If the half-life of the parent is considerably shorter than that of the daughter, the former rapidly transforms into the latter, which then decays with its own decay constant. If the half-life of the parent is considerably longer than that of the daughter, after certain time greater than the half-life of the daughter, an equilibrium is established. Then the number of decays of two substances is approximately equal.

Between these two cases there are intermediate ones where the difference between λ_1 and λ_2 is not very large.

5. Production of Radionuclides

When a material is irradiated in a reactor or accelerator, the radioactive isotopes are produced at a constant rate. Since to a constant rate corresponds an infinite half-life, the production of radioactive nuclides can be treated mathematically as a two-member series in which the first member has a half-life $T_{1/2}^1$ tending to infinity and making $\lambda_1 = 0.693/T_{1/2}^1$ very small. As the number of atoms in the target N_1^0 is relatively very large, the product $\lambda_1 N_1^0$ is finite, and the equation (28) becomes

$$N_2 = \lambda_1 N_1^0/\lambda_2 \, [1 - \exp(-\lambda_2 t)] \tag{29}$$

By multiplying with λ_2 we obtain the activity of produced radioactive nuclide $A = \lambda_2 N_2$ equal to

$$A = \lambda_1 N_1^0 [1 - \exp(-\lambda_2 t)] \qquad (30)$$

The probability of formation of radioactive nuclei depends on the intensity of the beam producing the reaction ϕ, and the cross-section for reaction σ. In the calculations, it is more convenient to deal with specific activities S defined by activity per gram of irradiated material. It is given by the relation

$$S = (0.6 \, \phi\sigma/M) [1 - \exp(-0.69 \, t/T_{1/2})] \qquad (31)$$

where
S   = number of disintegrations per second or becquerels
ϕ = particles flux/(unit of surface)^2/sec
σ = excitation cross-section in (barns) $10^{-28}m^2$
M   = atomic weight of bombarded element
t   = irradiation time
$T^{1/2}$ = half-life of the radionuclide (in same units as t)

G. Statistics of Measurement

The exponential decay curve which we obtained for the activity of a radioactive source is of statistical nature, so that the values of measured activity do not fall exactly along that curve. The measured points are scattered over, on, and below the smooth exponential curve. When one starts with measured points and has to draw a continuous curve through them, it is necessary to have a knowledge of radioactive measurement statistics. They are valid in any other measurement of radioactive radiations, such as for example the study of energy spectra or penetration through matter.

A convenient way to approach statistics is to take a long-lived radioactive source and to measure the number of decays in a time interval t which is negligibly short as compared to the half-life. If the measurements are repeated under the same conditions, the number of decays n will fluctuate about a mean value $\bar{n}$. The probability of observing a given number of counts n in the time interval t, which we denote by P_n is given by the expression

$$P_n = (\bar{n}^n/n!) \, e^{-\bar{n}} \qquad (32)$$

where $\bar{n}$ is the average value of n, which can be obtained in a very large number of measurements:

$$\bar{n} = (n_1 + n_2 + n_3 \ldots n_s)/s \qquad (33)$$

The expression for P_n represents a statistical function known as Poisson distribution, which is illustrated in Figure 10. We might observe that P_n consists of an exponential funcion $e^{-\bar{n}}$ multiplied by a factor $\bar{n}^n/n!$ which transforms it into a curve of a bell shape type.

We can connect the Poisson distribution (32) with the decay law (24) by making $n = 0$, which gives

$$P_0 = e^{-\bar{n}} \qquad (34)$$

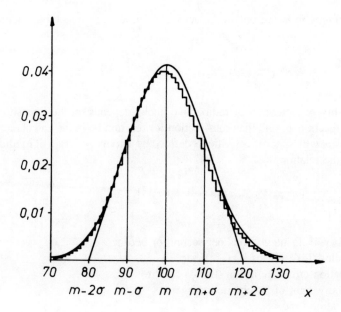

FIGURE 10.   The Poisson distribution, shown as a histogram, and corresponding normal distribution for $\bar{n} = m = 100$.

This is equivalent to (24) for $N_0 = 1$ and $n = \lambda t$, which means that $P_0 = e^{-\lambda t}$ is the probability that one atom will survive without decay for a time t. If we have N_0 atoms, we get by multiplying (34) with N_0, that $P_0 N_0 = N$ atoms shall on the average survive after a time t.

The same reasoning is valid for penetration of a narrow beam of photons through matter. Then μ is the probability for a photon to have a collision over a unit distance, μx is the average number of collision along a path length x, and $e^{-\mu x}$ is the probability that a photon will travel a distance x without a collision. By multiplying with intensity of photon beam N_0 we obtain the number of photons N which do not collide over the distance χ

$$N = N_0 e^{-\mu x} \tag{35}$$

1. Normal Distribution

The Poisson distribution is defined only for positive integer values of n, and has a shape of a histogram. For a large number of n it can be transformed into a limiting continuous function called normal distribution or gaussian error curve

$$P_n = (2\pi\bar{n})^{-1/2} e^{-(n-\bar{n})^2/2\bar{n}} \tag{36}$$

The Poisson and normal distributions are illustrated in Figure 10. The advantage of normal distribution is that the usual error parameters are better displayed.

2. Standard Error

The most often used parameter to define the error of radiation measurements is the standard deviation σ. It is defined as the root-mean-square deviation from the average

$$\sigma^2 = \frac{\sum_{n=0}^{\infty} (\bar{n}-n)^2 P_n}{\sum_{n=0}^{\infty} P_n} \qquad (37)$$

which can be easily transformed to

$$\sigma^2 = \bar{n} \qquad (38)$$

Since in the single measurement we do not know the average value $\bar{n}$, while the measured value $\bar{n}$ should not differ much from it, especially when n is high, we can take n for $\bar{n}$ and obtain

$$\sigma = \sqrt{n} \qquad (39)$$

We then present our measured value as

$$n \pm \sigma \qquad (40)$$

We can see from Figure 10 that the area between $\bar{n} + \sigma$ and $\bar{n} - \sigma$ represents 68% of the total area under the normal distribution curve. It means that if we make a large number of measurements, 68% of them would fall within $\bar{n} \pm \sigma$. When one has to draw a line through measured points, it is necessary to keep in mind that one out of three points is more than $\sqrt{N}$ off the mean value.

It is important to note that the error decreases with the increase of n. For n = 100 the standard deviation σ is 10%, decreasing to 1% for n = 10,000. The other statistical parameters, which can be used, are

probable error	0.6745σ
reliable error	1.60σ
95% confidence limit	1.97σ

3. Counting Losses

Every detection process, in which single particles are counted, takes a certain time. For that reason there is a minimum time interval between two counting, which is called the resolving time τ. If a particle enters the counter while the detection process of the previously entered particle is not completed, it would not be detected. Thus the registered number of counts n' is smaller than the number of particles n which entered the detector. A correction has to be made for counting losses.

If the observed number of counts per second is n' and the resolving time is τ sec, then the fraction of unit time during which the detector was not able to count is $n'\tau$ and the fraction of particles which were not counted is $nn'\tau$. The counting rate n' is then equal to

$$n' = n - nn'\tau$$

$$= n(1 - n'\tau)$$

and $\qquad n = n'/(1 - n'\tau) \qquad (41)$

The counting losses increase with the intensity of radiation, and if it is very high then our simple linear relation (41) is not valid any more. It is advisable to keep $n'\tau$ below 0.05.

The resolving time τ differs widely between the detectors, from 10^{-4} sec for Geiger counters to 10^{-8} sec for some scintillation counters. It should be experimentally evaluated for a given recording instrument.

IV. NUCLEAR REACTIONS

A. Introduction

The unstable nuclides are obtained by bombarding the stable nuclides with beams of particles which are produced either in accelerators or in nuclear reactors. The accelerator represents one of the fastest growing instruments in our age of fast technology growth. In about 50 years the energies which can be produced in the accelerators have increased by a factor of one million, and the types of particles which are being accelerated have enormously diversified. In the beginning only ions of the isotopes of the two lightest elements — hydrogen and helium — were used, while now any element, usually multiply ionized, can be accelerated. The heavy ion physics is, indeed, spearheading the nuclear investigations at the present moment.

The radioactive isotopes can be produced with every accelerator presently available and every kind of particle beam. As the energy of the particle beam increases, more neutrons can be expelled from a given stable nucleus and a number of neutron deficient radionuclides are obtained which need several beta decays before returning to the stability line. The fact that one obtains several radionuclides, instead of the one needed, and that in most cases a series of decays are in course, usually do not represent desirable features for radionuclide use. If one adds a highly increased cost factor, it is understandable why the production of radionuclides for medical use is confined to lower energy accelerators, mainly cyclotrons, accelerating alpha-particle, deuterium, and proton beams to energies below 30 MeV.

The radionuclides produced by accelerated charged particles are complementary to those produced by neutrons in the nuclear reactors. When a neutron is added to a nucleus, it usually transforms one of its neutrons into proton expelling a negative beta-particle. On the other hand, when a charged particle from the accelerator enters a nucleus, a proton is usually transformed into a neutron and either a positive electron is emitted, or an electron capture takes place, in which photons carry away most of the decay energy. Quite generally, the reactor produced radioactive nuclides are mostly used when local ionization by electrons is of interest, while cyclotron-produced radioisotopes are useful for obtaining photon signals about the localization of radioactive nuclide. In addition, we obtain in reactor strong gamma sources, such as Co-60.

B. Processes in the Target

When a beam of charged particles bombards a target, several processes can occur:

1. Beam particles collide with atomic electrons producing *ionizations* and *excitations* of atoms and molecules in the target. The energy of the beam particles thereby decreases, while the part of energy transferred to the target dissipates finally into heat.
2. The probability of collision with relatively very small nuclei is much smaller compared to the collision with electrons. If the particle does not come into a close interaction with the nucleus, an *elastic nuclear collision* might take place, in which a part of particle's kinetic energy is transferred to the nucleus, setting it in motion as a whole. Most of the energy of the moving atom is also dissipated as heat. The internal state of the nucleus remains unchanged.
3. A still closer interaction with the nucleus may produce internal disturbances, in a way

similar to those taking place in the electron cloud (excitations and ionizations). The energy received from the bombarding particle may be used for excitation of the nucleus. This is called *inelastic nuclear scattering*. The deexcitation takes place usually in a very short time, with the emission of one or more gamma rays.

4.   Another possibility is that the bombarding particle is absorbed by the nucleus with the result that its released binding energy brings the nucleus into a highly excited state. The deexcitation can take place in two different ways: (1) Several gamma rays may carry off the excitation energy. The final result is that the incoming particle was *captured* and a new nucleus is formed, which is radioactive. The most interesting case, for the radionuclide production is the *neutron capture,* which is symbolically shown as (n,γ). (2) The excitation energy of the nucleus may be concentrated on one or more of its constituents, which can then leave the nucleus. If alpha-particles are accelerated, they can expel in simplest cases a proton or a neutron or two neutrons, which is symbolically shown by brackets (α,p), $\alpha,n)$ or $(\alpha,2n)$. As a rule, in these cases also, a radioactive nucleus is produced. A general name, for both alternatives is *nuclear reaction.*

Summarizing, we should point out three limitations regarding the radionuclide production:

1.   Target heating. Much of the beam energy is spent in heating the target. An efficient cooling is necessary and the dimensions of target are also limited.
2.   Beam energy loss. Since the nuclear processes are usually very sensitive to energy, one can choose the best beam energy, but as the beam penetrates through the target, its energy is rapidly decreasing. One has to integrate over an energy interval.
3.   "Impurities". More than one reaction is often possible with a single nuclide, the probabilities being very different. Very often the irradiated element consists of several stable nuclides, so that the number of produced radioactive nuclides is proportionally increased. The target may also contain various kinds of impurities due to preparation process and environment. After the irradiation the target would contain, as a rule, several radioactive nuclides.

C. Energies in the Reaction

The minimum energy required for a nuclear reaction to occur is determined by principles of conservation of energy and of momenta. The balance of masses plus energies before and after the reaction is named "Q-value" and can be defined as

Q = (Sum of atomic masses of reactants) − (Sum of at. masses of products)

The reaction is exoergic when Q is positive, and endoergic for negative Q. In the first case energy is liberated, while for endoergic reaction −Q represents a part of energy which must be brought to the system from the outside beam.

An additional kinetic energy also has to be brought in, because when a beam particle of mass m strikes the target nucleus of mass M, a part of the momentum is transferred from the former to the latter. It follows from the principle of conservation of momenta that Q-value has to be increased by a factor $(m + M)/M$, so that the minimum required kinetic energy T_m is given by

$$T_m = -Q\,(m + M)/M \qquad\qquad (42)$$

It is seen that T_m depends on the ratio m/M.

D. Reaction Cross-Sections

The design and interpretation of a nuclear reaction experiment requires three different kinds of information:

1. Initial physical and geometrical conditions. First we should know quantitatively what are the particles in the beam, their mean energy and energy spread, and the geometry of the beam. Next, we should know chemical composition of the target, its physical characteristics and its geometry. Finally, we should know what happened during the experiment to parameters that could vary, such as the beam intensity and energy.
2. The results of experimental measurements. We usually have to establish at least one of the following parameters: intensity, energy, kind of particles or systems, and the angles of emission, if it is taking place.
3. Laws and models. When preparing the experiment one always knows, more or less, the physical laws governing the processes, which one expects that should take place. The degree and the precision of our knowledge might vary very much. In general, we expect to learn something new in a fundamental experiment, and we should know all we need in a radionuclide producing reaction. Our knowledge might be just at the level of empirical law, or at higher degree of a theoretical model, or finally, we might possess an adequate theory. Whatever our knowledge might be, we have to use it in design and interpretation of experiment. The mathematical treatment of experiment has to integrate all three sets of information.

The most important question for interpretation may be reduced to what happens when one particle of the beam interacts with one system of the target, a nucleus, or an atom. What we know about it is expressed in the probability for a given process, which we denote by σ. Since in nuclear processes we are mostly interested in nuclear forces which are confined to nuclei, a nuclear reaction is taking place mainly when the particle enters the nucleus. Geometrically, an incoming particle 'sees' the cross-section of the nucleus, and the larger the cross-section the more probable is their interaction. For that reason the probability of interaction of one particle with one target system is called cross-section σ, has the dimensions of a surface, and a unit is chosen approximately equal to the cross-section of a nucleus, which is (1 barn =) $10^{-28} m^2$.

The cross-section σ contains the information from our third set — the laws and models. Their numerical values are obtained by using some information from the first set: what are the particles, their initial energies and the initial geometry.

When the determination of σ is completed, we continue with information from the first set which are needed to pass from the interaction of one particle with one target system, to the interaction of a beam with macroscopic target.

Suppose that there are N_0 target systems per unit area, and that their number is relatively so small that an incoming particle can 'see' them all, none of them being hidden behind the system. Then, the probability that one particle per unit area and unit time shall interact with N_0 systems per unit area is equal to σN_0.

If the beam contains I particles per unit area and unit time, the number of interactions dI is given by

$$dI = I \, \sigma \, N_0 \qquad\qquad (43)$$

Three-dimensional clarifications should be added. The number of targets per unit area N_0 is equal to the number of atoms per unit volume, multiplied by the thickness of the target. The number of atoms per unit volume can be expressed by density, atomic mass, and Avogadro's number. Care should be taken to differentiate between the old and new units.

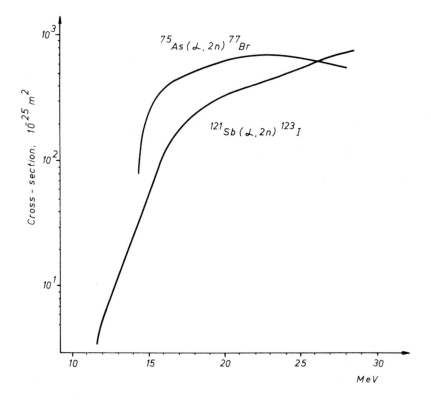

FIGURE 11. The excitation curves for production of ⁷⁷Br and ¹²³I by alpha-particles in a cyclotron.

Equation 43 is valid for the density of the beam per unit surface. In order to get the total number of interactions, a multiplication by the surface of the cross-section of the beam is needed.

We have supposed that the target is thin, so that the beam 'sees' all the atoms. The incoming particle does not produce a nuclear reaction with every nucleus that it sees. The thinness of the target depends on σ.

E. Excitation Curve

A nuclear reaction, like any other process in nature depends on the energy in a selective way. A curve showing how the probability of occurrence of a nuclear reaction depends upon the energy of the bombarding particle is called excitation curve or function. It represents the cross-section for a given reaction as a function of the energy of the incident particle. Since often more than one reaction is possible, the excitation curves permit the calculation of relative reaction yields for a given energy interval. Figure 11 illustrates two kinds of excitation curves for the production of radionuclides in a cyclotron.

F. Nuclear Models

Our knowledge of nuclear forces is not sufficient for an exact description of various processes which take place when nuclei are bombarded by accelerated particles. The approximate treatment is done with the help of models, which usually represent partial and simplified pictures of nuclear behavior within a given range of nuclear parameters. They are often built on analogy and described in a way which helps the visualization of related processes. There are three important models in low energy nuclear reactions.

One possibility is that the incident particle is scattered in such a way that it feels nucleus as a whole. The process is similar to the scattering of light by a crystal ball. Since some intensity is lost in the ball, as if it were clouded, an early name of this process was *cloudy crystal ball model*. A characteristic of this model is that, just as with the scattering of light, there are interference effects, with maxima and minima of cross-sections. The less picturesque name for this model is *optical model*.

The next possibility is that the incident particle reacts with only one or two nucleons in the nucleus. Such a process becomes probable when the interaction between the incident particle and the target nucleus takes place close to the surface of the nucleus. They have been named *direct processes*. An interesting example of direct process is the deuteron stripping. Since deuteron is a relatively loosely coupled system, the nuclear electrostatic barrier may repel the proton, while neutron is dissociated and enters the nucleus, leading to a reaction of (d,p) type.

The third important possibility is that the incident particle has many collisions inside the nucleus, and when it has lost the excess energy, it remains in the nucleus, forming a highly excited new nuclide. This has been called the *compound nucleus model,* and is of primary importance in radionuclide producing reactions. For that reason we shall confine our attention only to this model.

1. Compound Nucleus Model

Nils Bohr proposed this model in 1936 as a two-step process. In the first step the incident particle delivers its energy to many nucleons in the target nucleus, and this energy is rapidly distributed throughout the nucleus. The incident particle itself becomes indistinguishable from other nucleons in the compound nucleus, and we can say that the compound nucleus 'forgets' the way in which it was formed.

Due to the forgetfulness of the compound nucleus, the second step is independent and unrelated to the first step. The excitation energy of the compound nucleus is equal to the kinetic energy introduced by the incident particle plus its binding energy. This energy is statistically distributed among the nucleons, and each nucleon is rapidly colliding with the others and changing its energy. It may happen that by chance enough energy is concentrated on one nucleon, or temporary systems of nucleons, such as alpha-particle, that they can leave the nucleus, and an emission takes place. In most cases the emitted particles are neutrons, protons, deuterons, alpha-particles, and photons. Often several emission modes are competing with various probabilities. The emission of gamma rays, for instance, is slow compared to the emission of particles, and on the other hand, the electrostatic barrier reduces appreciably the probability of the emission of a charged particle, compared to neutron emission.

The compound nucleus model predicts angular and energy relations different from direct interaction, so that the measurements reveal what process is taking place. In the case of compound nucleus, the angles of emission are all equally probable, while they are correlated with the incoming beam, in the case of direct interactions. The energies are also distributed in a different way, because compound nucleus emission resembles the evaporation of molecules from the surface of a liquid, while direct processes do not include that kind of statistical distribution.

The total probability for nuclear reaction via compound nucleus formation can be obtained by calculating separately both steps. An important factor in the first step is the relation between the excitation energy and the energy levels of the compound nucleus. When these two energies are close to each other, a phenomenon known in several branches of physics as resonance can take place.

a. Resonance Processes

A nucleus does not accept indiscriminately any excitation energy, but only those values

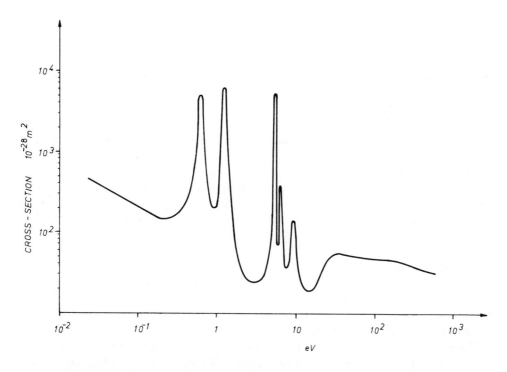

FIGURE 12. The resonant structure of cross-section for cobalt irradiated by neutrons.

which can bring it into one of possible discrete excited states. The first step of the reaction depends on the nature of excited states, which vary with the energy and mass number A in the following way:

- The separation between the adjacent excitation levels decreases with increasing energy of excitation and increasing A.
- The level width, measuring the sharpness of energy values which can excite a given energy level increases on the average with the excitation energy. Less precise energies can excite higher levels.
- The level width is, according to the Heisenberg uncertainty equation inversely proportional to the half-life of the level.
- For sufficiently high excitation energies and (or) high A, the level width increase and the level spacing decrease may produce the overlapping of levels. Then a discrete excited state of compound nucleus cannot be formed even for a very short time, and the compound nucleus model ceases to be useful.

When the conditions are such that the levels are separated, the probabilities of compound nucleus formation, given as function of incident particle kinetic energy, shows prominent maxima of cross-section. Such kind of energy selective enhancement of nuclear reaction is called nuclear resonance. Figure 12 shows an example of resonant variation of cross-section.

2. Neutron Reactions

A classification of neutrons according to energy has been developed in practice and the following five groups of energy range denominations are commonly used:

- *Fast* neutrons, 0.5 to 20 MeV

- *Intermediate* neutrons, 0.3 to 500 keV
- *Resonant* range, 1 to 300 eV
- *Slow* neutrons, 1 to 10 eV
- *Thermal* neutrons are in the thermal equilibrium with matter at a given temperature, and their energy follows a statistical (Maxwell) distribution. For a temperature of 20°C the maximum of the energy distribution is at 0.0252 eV.

We shall now consider briefly the main types of interaction of neutrons with nuclei.

a. Elastic Scattering

The energy loss of neutrons in an elastic collision with a nucleus is inversely proportional to their mass difference, and to the square of its speed. This process is therefore important for light materials and for neutrons of lower energies. For intermediate neutrons, the elastic scattering represent by far the most important mode of interaction with nuclei.

b. Inelastic Scattering

A part of kinetic energy of incident particle is transferred to a nucleus, which remains in the excited state for a very short time. After some time, which depends on energy and spin changes and may range between 10^{-14} to 10^{-6} sec, the excitation energy is emitted from the nucleus in a form of gamma rays.

The inelastic scattering is important for fast neutrons and becomes negligible at energies of the order of 100 kV. It is also more probable for heavy nuclei, where nuclear level spacing is smaller.

c. Nuclear Reactions

The ejection of charged particles from the nucleus requires much less energy in the case of the lightest nuclei, where electrostatic barrier is the lowest. An important nuclear reactions produced by neutrons is

$$^{10}B \, (n,\alpha) \, ^{7}Li$$

It is an exoergic reaction with an energy release of 2.78 MeV. The alpha-particle carries a larger part of available energy, which is convenient for detection. The cross-section for this process is inversely proportional to the neutron velocity, from thermal neutrons to about 30 keV. The cross-section for thermal neutrons is very high, amounting to 3840 barns. Figure 13 shows the cross-section of boron for neutrons.

d. Neutron Capture

The chance for a neutron to remain in the nucleus, without expelling any other particle, increases at very low energies, and becomes prominent in resonant and thermal regions. In many cases, this is a final event by which a free neutron ends its penetration through matter. The excitation energy is released in the form of several gamma rays.

The reactor produced radionuclides are obtained by (n,γ) reaction. We present in Table 12 some of the reactor-produced radionuclides used in medicine.

V. PENETRATION OF RADIATION IN MATTER

Every experiment with radiation represents in essence a succession of processes of interaction between radiation and matter. The knowledge of these processes is necessary for design and interpretation of experiment. It is sufficient to mention such constitutive elements

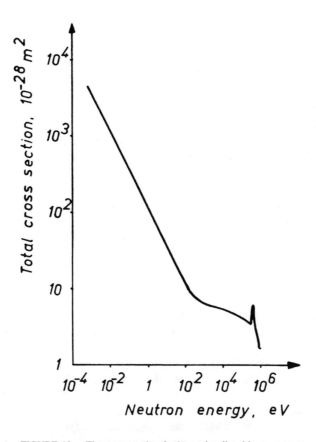

FIGURE 13. The cross-section for boron irradiated by neutrons.

Table 12
RADIOISOTOPES USED IN MEDICINE, PRODUCED BY
(n,γ) REACTIONS IN NUCLEAR REACTORS

Isotope	Half-life	Cross-section for natural element in 10^{-28} m²	Specific activity B_q/kg for a flux of 10^{16} n/cm² sec⁻¹ — 1 week radiation	Saturation activity
^{24}Na	15 hr	0.53	1.4×10^{12}	1.4×10^{12}
^{35}S	87.4 days	0.011	9.6×10^{8}	2×10^{10}
^{38}Cl	37.3 m	0.138	2.3×10^{11}	2.3×10^{11}
^{42}K	12.4 hr	0.069	1×10^{11}	1×10^{11}
^{45}Ca	165 days	0.013	4.8×10^{8}	1.95×10^{10}
^{56}Mn	2.6 hr	13.2	1.44×10^{13}	1.44×10^{13}
^{55}Fe	2.68 years	0.128	5.2×10^{8}	1.37×10^{11}
^{60}Co	5.27 years	36	8.14×10^{10}	3.66×10^{13}
^{64}Cu	12.7 hr	2.7	2.55×10^{12}	2.55×10^{12}
^{65}Zn	244 days	0.244	3.7×10^{9}	2.26×10^{11}
^{82}Br	35.3 hr	1.7	1.18×10^{12}	1.26×10^{12}
^{86}Ru	18.8 days	0.52	7.4×10^{10}	5.38×10^{11}
^{134}Cs	2.06 years	26	5.8×10^{10}	1.26×10^{13}
^{170}Tm	128 days	130	1.44×10^{12}	4.6×10^{13}
^{198}Au	2.69 days	96	2.3×10^{13}	3×10^{13}

of the majority of experiments, as the irradiation effects, the detection of and the protection from radiations.

We shall briefly consider basic properties of interaction of alpha, beta, and gamma rays with matter.

A. Alpha-Particles
1. Nature of Alpha-Particle Track

In some detecting media the ionizations produced by alpha rays serve as nuclei for formations of visible particles which show the paths of alpha rays. These visible tracks have the following properties:

1.   In most cases, the alpha-particle track is rectilinear
2.   The track becomes tortuous only near its end
3.   A monokinetic source gives tracks of approximately the same length
4.   There is about 1% fluctuation in track lengths
5.   There is no appreciable absorption of particles along the track

2. Stopping Power

The stopping power of an absorber is defined as the energy loss dE per unit path length dx. The following are the main characteristics of alpha-particle energy losses:

1.   Energy loss in bremsstrahlung is negligible.
2.   The energy loss in collisions with nuclei is also negligible. For example, when E < 0.5 MeV, the energy loss in collision with nuclei is 500 times smaller than the energy loss in ionization and excitation.
3.   For energies below 1 to 2 MeV, the alpha-particle captures one or two electrons, which start orbiting and thus transforms into once ionized helium ion or neutral helium atom. In subsequent collision it can loose them and pick up again. While this is going on, its effective charge is less than $Z = 2$. The theory becomes then more involved and experimental data more useful.
4.   For energies higher than 2 MeV the stopping power can be considered to be due only to the energy loss in inelastic collisions with electrons, and the theoretical formulae hold. They have now achieved an accuracy of about 1%.

The tables of stopping power are available, and if more precision is needed, any special value can be calculated in a computer.

3. Specific Ionization

The specific ionization is defined as the total number of ions produced by the ionizing particle per unit path length. It is obtained by dividing the mean energy loss with the value of energy expended to produce an ionization. As the energy of alpha-particle is decreased, the specific ionization increases, and in the air the maximum is achieved at about 700 keV, when the specific ionization is about 6600 ion pair/mm of air. After this maximum the specific ionization decreases abruptly.

4. Range

In using radioactive radiation it is often useful to know the path lengths, which are proportional to particle energy. The quantities associated with the track lengths are denoted by the common term 'range'. There are several definitions of range, depending on what is measured or calculated. The differences are due to statistical character of energy loss and the deflection of particles.

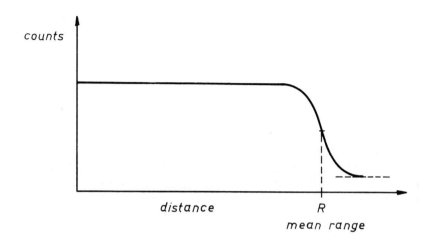

FIGURE 14.   The transmission curve for alpha-particles.

In the majority of experiments one is not interested in the true lengths of particle tracks, but rather the depth of particle penetrations along the beam direction. The mean value of penetration depths of many particles is called the projected range or simply range.

The measurement of projected range of a collimated beam of alpha-particles is shown in Figure 14. After a flat part of the counting rate curve there is a gradual decrease at the end. A *mean range* can be defined as the length of absorber which reduces the counting rate by a half.

The mean projected ranges can be found in tables. The mean range of alpha-particles is relatively short, being 3.5 cm in air and 0.006 cm in aluminum for an energy of 5 MeV.

B. Electrons
1. The Nature of Electron Tracks
The electrons having an energy below 10 MeV have the following track characteristics:

1.   The electron track is approximately linear only at energies above 1 MeV. The deflections increase with decreasing energy and finally the motion turns over into the diffusion.
2.   The fluctuations of track lengths are greater in the case of electrons than in that of alpha-particles.
3.   The penetration depth for majority of electrons in a beam is considerably smaller than their track lengths.

2. Bremsstrahlung
Since electrons are light and fast particles, their penetration through matter is accompanied by a production of bremsstrahlung. Two aspects of this process have to be mentioned: (1) the bremsstrahlung represents electromagnetic radiation which is more penetrating than electrons. For example, a pure beta emitter produces X-rays in the surrounding materials and in the shielding. Since this penetrating radiation is usually undesirable, the materials and shielding should be chosen to minimize it. (2) The bremsstrahlung production increases with the increase of electron energy and Z of absorber. The energy losses due to bremsstrahlung become more important than ionization losses for energies higher than 7 MeV if absorber is lead, while in aluminum the bremsstrahlung becomes dominant at electron energies higher than 47 MeV.

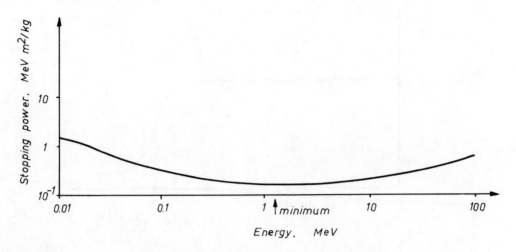

FIGURE 15.   The stopping power of electrons in aluminum.

The mean energy losses of positrons may differ from that of electrons by a few percent. At energies below 200 keV the energy loss of positrons is larger than that of electrons, whereas at higher energies we have the opposite case. Extensive tables of electron energy losses are available. The curves of mean energy losses of electrons show a minimum at an energy of about 1.5 MeV (Figure 15).

3. Specific Ionization
The curve of the specific ionization by electrons in air has a maximum of 770 ion pairs/ mm at an energy of 150 eV, which is about ten times weaker than ionization by alpha-particles. The minimum specific ionization by electrons at an energy of 1.5 MeV is only 5 ion pairs/mm of air (at normal pressure and temperature).

4. Range
We shall first consider the mean projected range of a collimated beam of *monoenergetic* electrons. The probabilities of large energy losses in electron-electron collisions are reflected in large fluctuations of true lengths of tracks. For projected ranges even more important are large angle scattering, especially in heavier absorbers.

The transmission curves of electrons do not show large plateau, corresponding to constant counting rate, as it is the case with alpha-particles. The counting rate starts decreasing almost since the beginning of the transmission, and this effect is more pronounced for heavier absorbers (Figure 16). In such transmission curves, the mean range has not much meaning, and the *extrapolated range* R_{ext}, constitutes more convenient measure of the projected range of the monokinetic electrons.

For *continuous* beta-ray spectrum the transmission curve greatly differs from that of a monokinetic beam. Since the beam contains electrons of energies from a certain maximum down to zero, those with lowest energies start diffusing immediately, lose their energy rapidly, and are stopped. This process advances progressively to electrons with higher initial energies and together with scattering, produces an approximately exponential decrease of the penetrating beam intensity.

The exact absorption curve depends on a number of factors, such as the shape of the beta spectrum, its maximum energy, Z of the absorber, and the geometry of the experiment. Because of its approximate character, it is impossible to define the extrapolated range and the only possibility left is to use the *maximum range,* R_{max}. It is defined as the length at

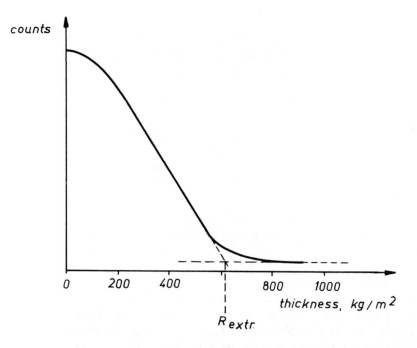

FIGURE 16.   The transmission curve of 250 keV electrons in aluminum.

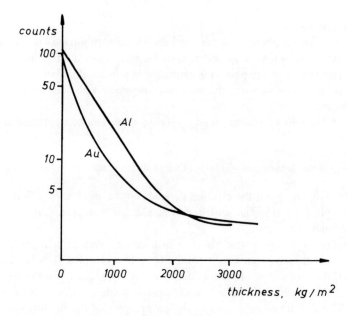

FIGURE 17.   The transmission curves for the continuous beta spectrum of [204]Te in Al and Au.

which beta-particles no longer reach the detector and only background radiation remains. It is not easy to determine with precision. Figure 17 shows absorption curves for [204]Tl in Al and Au.

It was experimentally established that the maximum range of a continuous spectrum is approximately equal to the extrapolated range of monokinetic electrons having an energy

Table 13
RANGE IN ALUMINUM OF
SOME OFTEN USED BETA
SOURCES

Nuclide	E_{max}, MeV	R_{max}, kg/m²
³H	0.018	0.0023
¹⁴C	0.155	0.20
³²P	1.701	8.10
⁹⁰Y	2.18	10.65
²¹⁰Bi(RaE)	1.17	5.08

equal to the maximum energy of the beta spectrum, so that the same empirical formulae and tables can be used. We give in Table 13 the range in aluminum of some frequently used beta-ray sources.

C. Electromagnetic Radiation

A photon is a quantum of electromagnetic field, and as such it can interact only with charged particles. If we put aside those charged particles that are produced only at high energies, the interactions of photons are limited to electrons and protons.

A collision between a photon and a system of charged particles can lead to two different kinds of processes—scattering and absorption. Although several processes are possible, only three are important: photoelectric effect, Compton scattering, and pair production.

1. The Photoelectric Effect

A collision between a photon and an electron bound to a nucleus in which the photon vanishes and the electron leaves the atom, is called photoelectric effect (often shortened to photoeffect). The energy of the photon is expanded in part for the liberation of the electron, whereas the rest is shared between the atom and the ejected photoelectron, as required by conservation laws.

In most cases the part of energy taken up by the atom can be neglected and the energy balance written as:

Energy of the photoelectron = Energy of the photon − Binding energy of the electron

Since the binding energy of the electron depends on the shell from which it was ejected, the energies of photoelectrons are distributed in a discrete sequence of values, and a line spectrum is obtained.

The probability for photoelectric effect is in a general way related to the conservation laws, which forbid the absorption of a photon by a free electron. The binding of electron being essential, the probability of photoeffect increases appreciably for more strongly bound shells. It is highest for K-shells which are closest to nuclei, and sharply increases with Z of the atom. The difference between the photon energy and the binding energy has to be shared by the atom and photoelectron. This seems to be easier for smaller differences, so that the probability of photoeffect is highest when this difference is nil.

The probability of photoelectric effect on the Z of the atom and photon energy E is roughly proportional to:

$$Z^{4.5}/E^3$$

2. The Compton Effect

A collision between a photon and a loosely bound electron, in which the photon transfers a part of its energy is called the Compton effect. It is in some ways complementary to photoeffect, since it occurs when the binding energy of ejected electron is negligible compared to photon energy. The nucleus is then not considered and the laws of conservation of energy and momentum are applied only to the photon and the Compton electron, regulating the angles of their emission and their energies.

The energy transferred to the electron is greatest when it is ejected forward and photon is scattered backward, while the lowest energy is transferred to the electron when the electron is ejected sidewise and the photon almost does not change its direction. The energy spectrum of Compton electrons is continuous, from a given maximum down to a value close to zero. At high photon energies E, the maximum energy of Compton electrons is

$$E - 0.255 \text{ MeV}$$

The Compton effect depends very roughly on Z and E as Z/E.

3. Pair Production

In this process, occurring in the electric field of a nucleus or of an electron, a photon vanishes and a pair, consisting of a positron and an electron, is produced. The probability of pair production is much higher in the electric field of the nucleus which has a much higher charge than unit charge of electron. One should notice that the principle of charge conservation is regulating the creation of charges from a noncharged photon.

The production of an electron pair requires an energy expenditure equal to two rest masses of electron, which is 1.02 MeV. The photon has to have an energy higher than 1.02 MeV, and the excess over that value is shared between the electron and the positron. Their energy spectra are, therefore, continuous.

The positron has a short life, just the time necessary to lose its kinetic energy, and then in an encounter with an electron, the pair is annihilated and two photons of 0.511 MeV each are produced.

The probability of pair production is roughly proportional to

$$Z^2 \ln E$$

This is the only one among three processes which increases with energy. The increase is logarithmic, which means rather slow.

We can see that each effect dominates in certain regions of E an Z:

1. The photoelectric effect dominates at low energies, especially for high Z
2. The Compton effect dominates at medium energies, especially for low Z
3. Pair production dominates at high energies, especially for high Z

4. Nature of Photon Penetration

The processes which we have just considered show that photons penetrate through matter in a way basically different from the charged particles penetration. The characteristics of photon penetration are

1. There is no ionized track marking the path of a photon. Its passage is marked by the track of ejected or created electrons. A photon of a few hundred kilovolts would eject a Compton electron, and then after some distance another Compton electron, and after may be one more ejections of Compton electron, it would be absorbed in a photoelectric

effect. In an appropriate detector one could see only a few electron tracks, at a distance from each other, and oriented sideways from the invisible photon path.

2.   Photons can be absorbed from the point of their emission along the whole of their path. When a collimated beam is considered, photons can be deflected out of the beam from the beginning of their penetration.

3.   The concept of range has no meaning in the penetration of photons. The depth of penetration does not depend only on the photon energy and the absorber, but also on the intensity of the beam. One has to operate with *half-value thickness* $x_{1/2}$, defined as thickness of absorber which reduces the intensity of a photon beam to one-half.

The penetration of a collimated photon beam is described by an exponential law:

$$n = n_0 \, e^{-\mu x}$$

where n_0 = initial number of photons; n = number of photons at depth x; and μ = linear attenuation coefficient. The half-value thickness is given by

$$x_{1/2} = 0.693/\mu \tag{44}$$

In many experiments, especially when designing the shielding for protection from radiation sources, the narrow beam geometry is not valid. The photons which are not emitted in the direction of the point where we want to reduce the radiation dose can be scattered towards that point. A broad beam can produce a dose two or three times larger than calculated for a narrow beam. The effect of the scattered beam is quantitatively represented by the buildup factor B, which is defined as

$$B = \frac{\text{effect produced by all photons}}{\text{effect produced by primary photons}}$$

The numerical values of buildup factors can be found in specialized literature.

GENERAL REFERENCES

1. **Evans, R.,** *The Atomic Nucleus,* McGraw-Hill, New York, 1955.
2. **Fano, U.,** Principle of radiological physics, in *Radiation Biology,* Vol. 1, Hollaender, A., Ed., McGraw-Hill, New York, 1954.
3. **Mladjenović, M.,** *Radioisotope and Radiation Physics,* Academic Press, New York, 1973.
4. **Wapstra, A. H., Nijh, G. J., and van Lishout, R.,** *Nuclear Spectroscopy Tables,* North-Holland, Amsterdam, 1959.
5. **Lederer, C. M. and Shirley, V. S., Eds.,** *Tables of Isotopes,* John Wiley & Sons, New York, 1978.
6. Studies in Penetration of Charged Particles in Matter, NAS — NRC Publication 1133, Washington D.C., 1964.

Chapter 3

ACTIVATION TECHNIQUES

Frank Helus and G. Wolber

TABLE OF CONTENTS

I. FUNDAMENTALS

A. Introduction

Isotopes are divided into two groups — stable and unstable, i.e., radioactive. The total known isotope number is about 1850, of which 280 are stable and the balance are radioactive,[1,2] having a transient existence ranging from the millionth of a second to millions of years. For the most part the radioactive nuclides are very short-lived. Radionuclides undergo transformation, or decay, emitting alpha, beta+, or beta‾ particles, or gamma or X-ray radiations during their return to a stable condition. Radionuclides are produced by disturbing a preferred neutron-proton ratio in the nuclei of elements. This is done by adding or removing charged particles such as protons (or many others) or by combination of both of them.

Isotopes, both stable and radioactive, have grown in importance to science and technology in the last 50 years. Since atoms can be marked by their radioactivity, or in some cases by an atypical isotopic composition, the elements can be traced — a procedure of great value in physical and biological science, technological and medical diagnostic. Radionuclides can perform many other tasks of benefit in today's complex industrial society.

The advent of cyclotrons and nuclear reactors has given rise to an abundance in both the quantity and variety of available radionuclides that have brought immense potentialities for scientific and technical use, and raised a host of new physical, biological, and medical problems. Further, the fast development of highly sensitive measuring techniques and equipment for radiation has made possible the development of beneficial uses of radionuclides as tracers in medical diagnostics. Developments in the last few years resulted in a significant movement towards cyclotron and generator-produced short-lived positron-emitting radionuclides and radiopharmaceuticals.

There are natural and manmade sources of radionuclides on this world.

B. Natural Sources of Radionuclides

Before artificial radioactivity was discovered[3,4] the only radionuclides available were the naturally occurring radionuclides ^{40}K, ^{50}V, ^{87}Rb, ^{113}Cd, ^{115}In and about 20 other elements which may be considered to be naturally radioactive. Further there are in nature heavy unstable elements such as ^{235}U, ^{238}U, and ^{232}Th and their decay products. They have been used in radiotherapy[5] and enabled foundations of isotope tracer techniques[6] to be laid. But their usefulness as tracers is restricted by the small number of chemical elements they represent and by the wide range of radiation energies they produced.

There are several natural sources of nucleons which can cause nuclear reactions on or near the earth. One such source is the spontaneous fission of very long-lived radionuclides such as ^{238}U, which, in addition to producing the radioactive fission products found in small quantities along with natural occurrences of uranium, gives rise to two or three neutrons per fission. These "fission neutrons" can then react with other nuclei to produce new nuclides. An example which is of particular significance to man is the reaction between neutrons and ^{238}U nuclei which is described in Figure 1. In this special case the nuclear reaction between a neutron and ^{238}U nucleus results in a very short-lived excited state ^{239}U nucleus, which decays to its ground state by gamma photon emission. This particular sequence of events, that is, neutron absorption and gamma emission, is very common and is usually written in the more concise shorthand of nuclear reaction as ^{238}U (n,γ) ^{239}U and the reaction called (n,γ) reaction. The same kind of shorthand is used for most other nuclear reactions.

Cosmic rays are a second important source of nucleons in our environment, which leads through nuclear reaction to the generation of radionuclides. Cosmic rays are showers of fast moving nucleons, electrons, and other fundamental particles. The atmosphere of our planet is continually bombarded by these particles and nuclear reactions are continually occurring between these nuclear particles and the atomic nuclei of our atmosphere. An example of

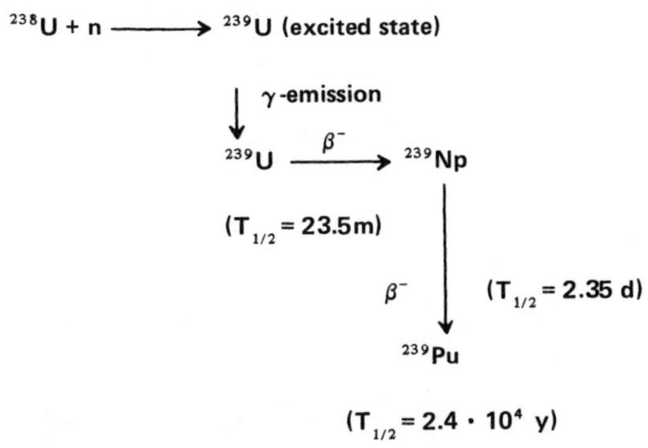

$$^{238}U + n \longrightarrow {}^{239}U \text{ (excited state)}$$

$$\downarrow \gamma\text{-emission}$$

$$^{239}U \xrightarrow{\beta^-} {}^{239}Np$$

$$(T_{1/2} = 23.5m)$$

$$\beta^- \downarrow \quad (T_{1/2} = 2.35 \text{ d})$$

$$^{239}Pu$$

$$(T_{1/2} = 2.4 \cdot 10^4 \text{ y})$$

FIGURE 1. Reaction between neutrons and U nuclei.

this source of natural radioactivity results from the reaction between neutrons and nitrogen nuclei — ^{14}N, which produces the radionuclide ^{14}C. This reaction — ^{14}N (n,p) ^{14}C is clearly accompanied by the emission of a proton. ^{14}C produced in this way enters the planet's carbon cycle from which some carbon ^{14}C may be trapped in a form which ceases to exchange with atmospheric carbon. The determination of the ^{14}C to ^{12}C (stable) ratio has become a useful technique for estimating the age of objects on 10^3 to 10^4 year time scale.

While the natural sources of radionuclides are of general interest (dating) and of considerable importance in many fields (uranium industry); the vast majority of radionuclides used now in laboratories are manmade. These radionuclides are without exception almost always produced by nuclear reactions using manmade sources of nucleons.

C. Manmade Radionuclides

The monumental discovery of radioactivity by Becquerel[7] was pivotal to the many fundamental discoveries in the physical and chemical sciences. In 1919, Rutherford's discovery of artificial radioactivity[4,8] achieved the feat vainly sought by ancient alchemists, that is changing one element into another. Rutherford bombarded nitrogen gas with alpha-particles. Some of the alpha-particles were absorbed by nitrogen, protons were emitted, and a different element, oxygen, was formed. It was nuclear reaction ^{14}N (α,p) ^{17}O. Curie and Joliot[3] had observed and identified the first artificially induced radioactivity in 1934 by irradiating aluminum with alpha-particles. The radionuclide produced was ^{30}P, using the nuclear reaction ^{27}Al (α,n) ^{30}P. In this genious short article they first demonstrated that nuclear bombardment could induce transmutations of some light elements to radioactive forms of other elements. This discovery offered the first chemical proof of artificial transmutation. After the introduction of the cyclotron by Lawrence[9,10] and other types of particle accelerators, many elements were bombarded with deuterons, protons, and other particles to produce hundreds of new radionuclides and it was the subsequent development of these machines that allowed them to obtain the radionuclides of most elements in useful quantities. This was also a very important step to exploit the radioactive isotopes for application as tracers in many scientific fields.

A second major source of manmade radionuclides has become available since the discovery of the first successful atomic pile chain reaction in 1942 by the group guided by Fermi[11] and followed development of nuclear fission reactors during the war years. Because of the secrecy of the Manhattan project during the second world war the produced radionuclides on the Oak Ridge and other reactors could not be admitted publicly. Reactor-produced radionuclides were available for public distribution since 1946.

A nuclear reaction is the reaction between a stable nucleus and a nucleon (which could

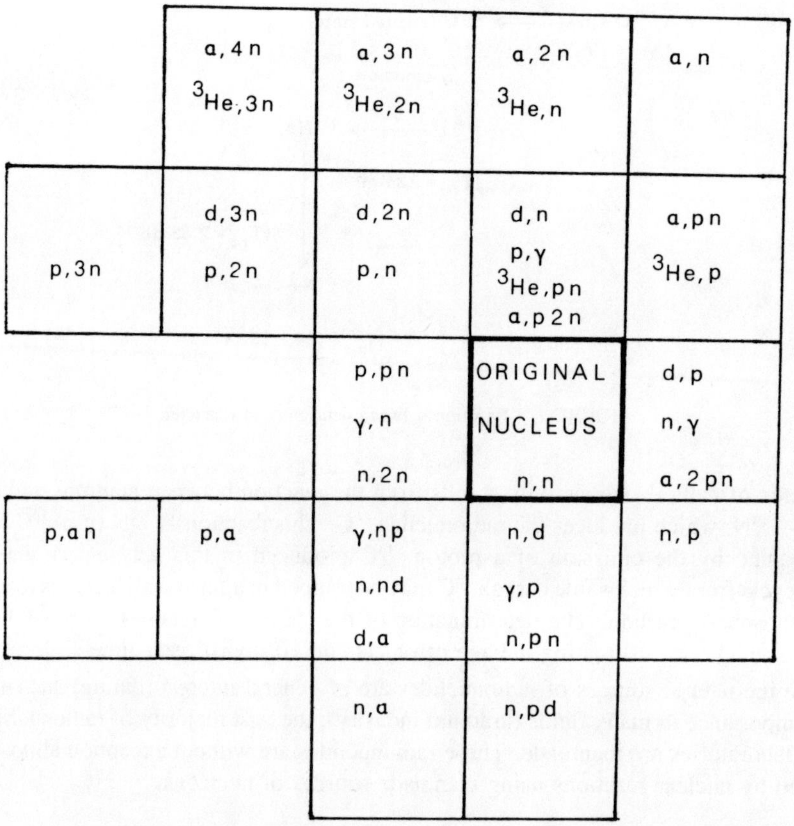

	$\alpha, 4n$ / $^3He, 3n$	$\alpha, 3n$ / $^3He, 2n$	$\alpha, 2n$ / $^3He, n$	α, n
$p, 3n$	$d, 3n$ / $p, 2n$	$d, 2n$ / p, n	d, n / p, γ / $^3He, pn$ / $\alpha, p2n$	α, pn / $^3He, p$
		p, pn / γ, n / $n, 2n$	ORIGINAL NUCLEUS / n, n	d, p / n, γ / $\alpha, 2pn$
$p, \alpha n$	p, α	γ, np / n, nd / d, α	n, d / γ, p / n, pn	n, p
		n, α	n, pd	

FIGURE 2.   Displacement of produced radionuclides caused by nuclear reactions with neutrons and light accelerated particles.

be neutron, proton, deuteron, alpha-particle, ^3He particle, or another nucleus) which results in the formation of a new nucleus. Different possible combinations of nuclear reactions and resulting changes of original nucleus by the action of incident and emitted particles is shown in Figure 2.

The most useful sources of incident nuclear particles (protons, deuterons, ^3He, and ^4He particles) are cyclotrons and other ion particle accelerators; and nuclear reactor and neutron generator as source for neutrons. These two machines are the primary source of radionuclides, and therefore the two techniques — reactor irradiation and cyclotron bombardment — are the most widely used routes to the manmade radionuclides, and nearly all commercially available radionuclides have been prepared in one of these ways.

A nuclear reactor is a facility in which a "fuel" such as natural uranium or uranium enriched in ^{235}U, ^{233}U, or ^{239}Pu, undergoes fission and produces heat, fission products and fission neutrons. Thus the nuclear reactors are the most useful sources of neutrons. Since a neutron has no electrical charge, there is no coulombic repulsion or attraction for orbital electrons or nuclei. It should be possible for neutrons of even very low kinetic energies to interact with target nuclei and cause nuclear reactions. Radioactive isotopes can be produced by several different neutron nuclear processes. Table 1 shows the different reaction mechanisms caused by thermal or fast neutrons.

The (n, γ) is the type of nuclear reaction which occurs most frequently. This activation gives, in general, so-called "neutron rich" radionuclides. These decay usually by the emission of negatively charged β-particles, often, but not necessarily accompanied by γ-radiation.

Table 1
REVIEW OF POSSIBLE REACTOR NUCLEAR
PROCESSES

I. Reaction induced by thermal neutrons.

I.A. Straightforward (n, ζ) reactions; most of reactor produced radionuclides are induced by this reaction. Practical examples are
seen in Table 2.

I.B. (n,p) reactions induced with thermal neutrons

reaction	$T_{1/2}$	Q	σ(mb)
$^{14}N(n,p)\,^{14}C$	5770 y	0.627	1.75
$^{33}S(n,p)\,^{33}P$	25 d	0.534	0.015
$^{35}Cl(n,p)\,^{35}S$	86.7 d	0.615	0.190

I.C. (n,α) reactions with thermal neutrons

$^{35}Cl(n,\alpha)\,^{32}P$	14.3 d	0.94	0.05
$^{54}Fe(n,\alpha)\,^{51}Cr$	27.8 d	0.82	0.37
$^{66}Zn(n,\alpha)\,^{63}Ni$	92.0 y	2.28	20.0 μb

II. Reactions induced by fast neutrons

II.A. (n,p) reactions

$^{24}Mg(n,p)\,^{24}Na$	15.0 h	7.20	1.20
$^{64}Zn(n,p)^{64}Cu$	12.9 h	4.80	39.00
$^{56}Fe(n,p)\,^{56}Mn$	2.58 h	7.40	0.87

II.B. (n,α) reactions

$^{27}Al(n,\alpha)\,^{24}Na$	15.0 h	8.80	0.56
$^{35}Cl(n,\alpha)\,^{32}P$	14.3 d	6.10	6.10
$^{68}Zn(n,\alpha)\,^{65}Ni$	2.56 h	10.20	0.033

Only the $^{6}Li(n,\alpha)\,^{3}H$ reaction has a practical importance.

III. Secondary reactions induced by tritons — ^{3}H from the $^{6}Li(n,\alpha)$
^{3}H or $^{6}Li(n,^{3}H)^{4}He$.
Practical use found only $^{16}O(^{3}H,n)^{18}F$ and $^{26}Mg(^{3}H,p)^{28}Mg$ secondary reactions.

Since the product nucleus of this type reaction, (n,γ), is a nuclide of target element, a chemical separation from the target material cannot generally be carried out. Thus, the specific activity obtainable by the (n,γ) reaction is limited, unless Szillard-Chalmers reaction[12] occurs. For most of (n,p) and (n,α) reactions, fast neutrons are required and the cross-sections for these types of neutron reactions are usually small and therefore the yields from these reactions are low. In these two cases the produced nuclide differs chemically from the target element and a chemical separation can be carried out and radioactive product of higher specific activity can be obtained. Table 2 lists some examples of typical routinely produced radionuclides in nuclear reactors.

The second source of radioactive products from the reactor are the fission products.[13,14] In the fission process an excited heavy nucleus may split into two nuclei of approximately equal size and this process is usually accompanied by the emission of neutrons. For example, when the ^{235}U or ^{239}Pu captures a neutron, fission may take place leading to a wide variety of fission product nuclei, many of which are radioactive. Hence it follows, the fission process as an inevitable consequence of reactor operation is a secondary source of certain radionuclides. The recovery of an appropriate radionuclide from the fission product mixture

Table 2
EXAMPLES OF TYPICAL ROUTINE REACTOR PRODUCED RADIONUCLIDES

Nuclide	$T_{1/2}$	Nuclear reaction	Cross-section	Target material
^{18}F	110 m	$^6Li(n,\alpha)^3H \rightarrow$	950.0 b	Li_2CO_3 enriched on ^6Li up to
		$^{16}O(^3H,n)^{18}F$	100.0 mb	98%.
^{24}Na	15.03 h	$^{23}Na(n,\gamma)^{24}Na$	30.53 b	Na_2CO_3, $NaHCO_3$
^{32}P	14.3 d	$^{31}P(n,\gamma)^{32}P$	0.18 b	Phosphor, KH_2PO_4
		$^{32}S(n,p)^{32}P$	0.06 b	Sulfur high purity
^{35}S	87.5 d	$^{35}Cl(n,p)^{35}S$	0.49 b	KCl
^{42}K	12.4 h	$^{41}K(n,\gamma)^{42}K$	1.46 b	K_2CO_3, $KHCO_3$
^{64}Cu	12.7 h	$^{63}Cu(n,\gamma)^{64}Cu$	4.50 b	Enriched ^{50}Cr or $^{50}Cr_2O_3$
		$^{64}Zn(n,p)^{64}Cu$	39.00 mb	Enriched ^{64}Zn
$^{85}\Sigma Kr$	4.48 h	$^{84}Kr(n,\gamma)^{85}\Sigma Kr$	0.09 b	Krypton gas
^{99}Mo	66.0 h	$^{98}Mo(n,\gamma)^{99}Mo$	0.13 b	Mo, MoO_3 enriched ^{98}Mo
^{113}Sn	115.0 d	$^{112}Sn(n,\gamma)^{113}Sn$	1.15 b	Enriched ^{112}Sn
^{131}I	8.04 d	$^{130}Te(n,\gamma)^{131}Te \downarrow 25$ m	0.29 b	Enriched ^{130}Te, or as fission
		^{131}I		product
^{133}Xe	5.29 d	$^{132}Xe(n,\gamma)^{133}Xe$	0.38 b	Enriched ^{132}Xe, or as fission
				product
^{198}Au	2.69 d	$^{197}Au(n,\gamma)^{198}Au$	98.80 b	Au metal

presents a complicated chemical problem, since the requested radionuclide represents only a small fraction of total activity which is so intense that the early process stages must be carried out entirely by remote control in shielded and completely enclosed cells. As an example of radionuclides obtained from the fission products could be shown ^{132}I, ^{133}Xe, and especially ^{99}Mo used as the first generator system[15] ^{99}Mo — ^{99m}Tc for preparation of ^{99m}Tc which found a wide application in nuclear medicine.

Most of the manmade radionuclides created by charged particles are produced by a cyclotron or other type of accelerator.[16] The cyclotron is essentially a high-voltage ion accelerator in which the ions are constrained to follow a spiral pathway by the presence of a magnetic field applied perpendicularly to the plane of ion motion (the principal of operation of the cyclotron and related accelerators are described later on). In general the radionuclides generated by charged particle bombardment are neutron defficient isotopes, and so tend to be those radionuclides which decay by β^+ emission-positron emitters; or decay by electron capture, or both. The nuclear reactions which occur on the cyclotron are varied and each nuclear reaction induced by charged particles has an optimum energy range for the bombarding particle, that produce the best results in terms of the yields or purity of desired product and minimum of co-produced contaminants. For some elements there is practically no reactor-produced radionuclide with properties suitable to make it of value as a tracer for biological studies. Some examples of radionuclides commonly produced at cyclotron installations are given in Table 3.

In some biomedical applications, the cyclotron-produced positron radionuclides are of exceptional interest. Use of ingenious positron devices can be applicated for observation of the distribution of positron-emitting radionuclides in the living organism and the observation of dynamic biological processes. In biological experiments one sometimes prefers to use a tracer material with a reasonably short half-life and typical biological elements such as ^{15}O, ^{13}N, and ^{11}C. Now there are more than 50 cyclotrons[17] dedicated to production of short-lived radionuclides which are directly used on the production site.

However there are several alternative radionuclide production routes which are of some importance, particularly for the production of relatively small quantities of short-lived nuclides in laboratories which do not have the facilities of a neighboring reactor or cyclotron.

Table 3
CYCLOTRON PRODUCED RADIONUCLIDES. SOME EXAMPLES OF RADIONUCLIDES CURRENTLY SUPPLIED FOR ONGOING PROJECTS FROM HEIDELBERG CYCLOTRON

Nuclide	Production reaction	Q-value	Target material	Production rate per batch	(mCi) per year	Delivered in chemical form
^{11}C	^{14}N(p,α)^{11}C	-2.9	N_2;99.99995%	1.5-2.0 Ci	54000	$^{11}CO_2$,H^{11}CN, etc.
^{13}N	^{16}O(p,α)^{13}N	-5.2	H_2O; 5 mℓ	250	28000	$^{13}NH_3$;$^{13}NH_3$-glutamate.
^{15}O	^{14}N(d,n)^{15}O	5.1	N_2; 99.99%	40	1400	$^{15}O_2$, H_2^{15}O, etc.
^{18}F	^{20}Ne(d,α)^{18}F	2.8	Ne; 99.99%	80-100	2100	Fluoride
^{38}K	^{40}Ca(d,α)^{38}K	-2.1	Ca metal	35	610	7^{38}KCl
^{81}Rb	^{82}Kr(p,2n)^{81}Rb	-14.2	Kr; 99.99%	50-60	2200	^{81}Rb-^{81}ΣKr generator
^{123}I	^{124}Te(p,2n)^{123}I	-11.2	$^{124}TeO_2$ enriched-96%	40-50	1700	Iodide
^{197}Hg	^{197}Au(p,n)^{197}Hg	-1.2	Au metal	2-3	60	$HgCl_2$

Two of these alternatives will be mentioned because of the relatively low costs associated with these methods of production. These are the neutron generators and the nuclide generators.

Neutron generator is a source of high energy — fast neutrons based on different principles.[18] Relatively inexpensive accelerators are available for the acceleration of deuterium ions to sufficiently enable the fussion reaction ^{3}H (d,n) ^{4}He to occur when deuteron beam strikes a solid target containing tritium. This reaction produces neutrons which have a high kinetic energy of about 14 MeV. These accelerators are so-called neutron generators and are used for the production of radionuclides and have been applicated with success in neutron therapy in oncology. In general, the neutron generators provide less neutron flux than fission reactors, so that the quantity of radionuclides obtainable with these accelerators is small and their main application is in the neutron therapy and activation analysis. (More details about this type of radionuclide production in Chapter 9).

The second means of obtaining a limited number of short-lived radionuclides in laboratory in some distance from reactor or cyclotron is the radionuclide generator.[19-21] A radionuclide generator is little more than a supply of moderately long-lived parent radionuclide which decays to produce a required short-lived radionuclide. Typical examples in Table 4 include generators used mostly in nuclear medicine.

Production of parent radionuclides for the preparation of radionuclide generators may be provided by either reactor (^{113}Sn-^{113m}In) or gained from fission products (^{99}Mo-^{99m}Tc), or produced by cyclotron (^{81}Rb-^{81m}Kr). In principal in most radionuclide generators the parent radionuclide is adsorbed on a support material, such as an ion exchange resin, which is packed in a small column. The short-lived daughter radionuclide may be eluted with different solvents (prefered are physiological solutions) from support material. There are many different systems based on different chemical separation methods as ion exchange, liquid extraction method, thermochemical separation, etc.

A special position between the radionuclide generators has ^{99}Mo-^{99m}Tc generator. ^{99}Technetium has been hailed with good reason as the ideal radionuclide for medical applications, possessing a single gamma photon of 140 keV and 6.02 hr half-life. ^{99m}Tc is distributed as its longer-lived parent ^{99}Mo. The ^{99}Mo is loaded as a solution of ammonium molybdate on an alumina chromatographic column. This generator can be eluted with isotonic

Table 4
SOME EXAMPLES OF COMMONLY USED RADIONUCLIDE GENERATORS

Generator	Parent nuclide	$T_{1/2}$	Decay mode	Intensity (%)	Daughter nuclide	$T_{1/2}$	Production method of the parent nuclide
^{62}Zn-^{62}Cu	^{62}Zn	9.25 h	β^+, EC	100.0	^{62}Cu	9.73 m	^{63}Cu(p,2n)^{62}Zn
^{68}Ge-^{68}Ga	^{68}Ge	287.0 d	EC	100.0	^{68}Ga	1.13 h	^{66}Zn(α,2n)^{68}Ge
^{77}Br-^{77m}Se	^{77}Br	57.0 h	EC	12.0	^{77m}Se	17.50 s	^{75}As(α,2n)^{77}Br
^{81}Rb-^{81m}Kr	^{81}Rb	4.58 h	β^+, EC	97.2	^{81m}Kr	13.30s	^{82}Kr(p,2n)^{81}Rb
^{82}Sr-^{82}Rb	^{82}Sr	25.0 d	EC	100.0	^{82}Rb	1.25 m	^{85}Rb(p,4n)^{82}Sr
^{99}Mo-^{99m}Tc	^{99}Mo	66.02 h	β^-	87.0	^{99m}Tc	6.02 h	^{98}Mo(n,γ)^{99}Mo and from fission products
^{109}Cd-^{109}Ag	^{109}Cd	453.0 d	EC	100.0	^{109}Ag	39.80 s	^{109}Ag(d,2n)^{109}Cd
^{113}Sn-^{113m}In	^{113}Sn	115.1 d	EC	100	^{113m}In	1.66 h	^{112}Sn(n,γ)^{113}Sn (enriched)
^{191}Os-^{191m}Ir	^{191}Os	15.4 d	β^-	100.0	^{191m}Ir	4.94 s	^{190}Os(n,γ)^{191}Os
^{195m}Hg-^{195m}Au	^{195m}Hg	40.0 h	EC, IT	50.0	^{195m}Au	30.60 s	^{197}Au(p,3n)^{195m}Hg

Note: Nuclear data are from Reference 1.

saline solution to remove ^{99m}Tc as required in the chemical form of pertechnetate ion. The product can be used in the eluted form, or labeled on different molecules in the form of kits. As the chemistry of Technetium is not simple, there are problems to use ^{99m}Tc for labeling of typical biomolecules and complicated organic molecules. Parent isotope ^{99}Mo could be produced by three different ways: (1) irradiation of enriched ^{98}Mo in high flux reactor over the reaction ^{98}Mo (n,γ) ^{99}Mo, (2) by separation from the fission products, or (3) by the irradiation of enriched ^{100}Mo with protons over the ^{100}Mo (p,pn) ^{99}Mo reaction at cyclotron.

The majority of users of radionuclides do not produce their own radioactivity. There is a very wide range of radioactive materials available commercially, either in the form of elemental radionuclides or as chemically labeled compounds with radionuclides at a specific place in the molecular structure. Several companies list a range of radionuclides and labled compounds among their products. The names of a number of suppliers are given in the appendix.

D. Target Definition

Generally, the radionuclides are produced by nuclear reaction (more details about nuclear reaction mechanism are in Chapter 2). A simple nuclear reaction can be noted as A (x,y) B + Q where A = target material nucleus; B = produced radioactive nuclei; x = bombarding particle; y = resulting particle; and Q = energy.

To produce the radionuclide B is the stable nuclide A present for irradiation (also activation or bombardment) in the form as target. Target may contain pure nuclide A or material which predominantly contains nuclide A, or finally artificially enriched nuclide A.

Target may be defined as follows: target material with target holder is the setup where the projectiles interact with target nuclei resulting in production of desired radioactive nuclide.

The word target is a term derived from military vocabulary. These terms such as target, projectile, bombardment, and others, have been adopted by scientists during the second world war, in the time of a rough progress of nuclear sciences and later development of nuclear weapons. Stetten[22] wrote in one article some interesting philosophical meditation on targets terminology. There are the analog problems, in the army or in the science; you can aim at the target and hit or miss it. There are several kinds of targets and it is the task of the scientist to choose which one could fulfill its duty — to hit exactly the goal — the appropriate element and produce economically and with all care of personnel the desired radionuclide. The actual production — irradiation or activation — is only a part of the problem. Having produced the short-lived radionuclide, the race to get it into the final system where it is to be used, starts with the removing of the target material from the reactor irradiation position or from the beam line on the cyclotron. Every step from this point on, must be planned and executed with the precision of a well-drilled military unit. All should be prepared and planned before the projectiles (nucleons) hit the target and if possible the operation should be trained in nonactive scale.

Shortly after the second world war, artificial radionuclides produced in reactors were made available for peaceful applications — the first shipment occurred on August 2, 1946 from Oak Ridge — the military terms used in nuclear science and radionuclide production terminology have not been changed. Possibly these terms are the most appropriate terms and therefore are generally used in scientific literature.

The target systems which are used on different sources of bombardment particles — reactors and accelerators — are for many reasons divided in common groups. The classification of the targets makes the basic characteristics of the targets more understandable.

For example, from the physical point of view, there are no fundamental differences in the procedure for radionuclide production by irradiating target material with neutrons in the nuclear reactor or with neutrons from the neutron generator using straightforward (n,γ) nuclear reaction on reactor, or over (n,γ) and (d,p) reactions on accelerator. However there is a great difference in target technique used for radionuclide production on these different facilities as the sources of neutrons.

According to the facility used as the source of projectiles, the targets for the radionuclide production may be broadly classified into two basic groups: (1) reactor targets and (2) cyclotron targets.

II. REACTOR TARGET SYSTEMS

The production of reactor radionuclides depends very much on the available neutron flux and the frequency and length of reactor operation time. With a typical reactor having a maximum flux of 10^{13} n/cm^2 sec of thermal neutrons and operated continuously for a minimum of 50 hr each week routine production of radionuclides can be performed. The establishment of routine production also involves many related problems, such as irradiations, measurement of radioactivity, pharmaceutical control, and problem with radioactive wastes.

Radionuclide production in the nuclear reactor may be subdivided into three major product classifications:

1. No chemically processed radioactive products produced and supplied in appropriate radiation shielding, but in the same form in which they were irradiated. For example, ^{14}Na is delivered in aluminum cans in the sodium bicarbonate form in which it was irradiated.
2. Radiochemically separated products, where after activation, the target material is processed in the chemical form which is specified by the user. All products in this group are mostly used in medical, biological research, and diagnostics. For example, the separation procedure used by production of ^{18}F[23,24] and labeling of organic compounds with ^{18}F.[25]
3. Radiation sources. In these products places primary importance on the emitted radiation and has no radioactive content in its chemical form. Examples are sealed alpha, beta, and gamma sources for therapeutical use and for other industrial applications.

The reactor target system consists of:

1. Target material
2. Irradiation capsules and containers; activation loops
3. Hydraulic or pneumatic target transfer systems
4. Target processing facility and chemistry

A. Target Material Requirements and Preparation

This section can be subdivided into two subgroups: (1) selection of the appropriate target material, and (2) preparation of target material for irradiation. As some aspects of target material selection for reactor irradiations differ from cyclotron bombardments, each type will be considered separately.

After determining the irradiation and production procedure, it is usual to select the most appropriate target material. For radionuclide procedures it is at first very important for all data to become available on target materials, irradiation conditions, application of the product, and nuclear reaction cross-sections.[26] The neutron reaction data have been extensively measured and evaluated due to needs in various fields, like fission reactors, breeder systems, etc. Under the term "nuclear reaction data" we placed all the data arising from interactions of nuclei with matter: elastic and nonelastic cross-sections; capture cross-section; total cross-section; excitation functions; fission yields; and microscopic data. Four regional data centers work actively on the compilation, evaluation, and dissemination of nuclear data, mainly neutron data, and data files exist on topics such as fission products, dosimetry, and activation, etc.

The nuclear data relevant to the production of radionuclides via neutron-induced reactions, especially in nuclear reactors, are known with fairly good accuracies. Nuclear data centers for compilation, evaluation retrieval, etc., are National Nuclear Data Center, Brookhaven, N.Y., USA, Nuclear Data Bank, NEA, Paris, (OECD Countries, Japan), Nuclear Cross-Section Center, Obninsk, (USSR), Nuclear Data Section, IAEA, Vienna.

One of the most important considerations for choosing a reactor target material is the safety, from the standpoint of preventing damage to the reactor, overheating of the target, rupture of the target, and developing gases in the target. The target material must be selected with great care to ensure the stability. The use of ultrapure materials is essential because the longer-lived radioactive impurities will be co-produced in samples by longer irradiations.

By the selection of appropriate target material for radionuclide production there are the following important factors:

1. The target material for the routine production should be readily available commercially. The metallic and elementary states are generally the best target materials. Favorable also are oxides, carbonates, and other appropriate chemical compounds which are mechanically and thermally adequately stable.
2. Thermal conductivity, chemical stability, and radiation decomposition of target materials should be considered before irradiation. If there is limited information in literature it is desirable to determine the physical and chemical stability of appropriate target material by preliminary experiments. The temperature which target material may reach during the irradiation at the intended position in the reactor should be estimated. The experimental irradiation should be carried out, starting with small amounts and steadily increasing.
3. All possible nuclear reactions in the target material should be surveyed. This means not only the radioactivity introduced by chemical impurities of the target element, but if chemical compound is used as target material then also the radioactivity induced from all other atoms (cations and anions). Activation analysis of the target material before the realization of production procedure is in many cases helpful. Before irra-

diation it is also very important to study all possible nuclear cross-sections and calculate the yield for the product and for all the possible co-produced radionuclides.

The general requirements for choosing and preparing the target material are mentioned above. Special considerations will be restricted to conditions affecting the target for the production of short-lived radionuclides:

1. The used target material must be chemically processed quickly and therefore it is sometimes preferable to use soluble compounds instead of metal target material.
2. Possible impurities have to be removed before the irradiation to minimize the purification after the irradiation on minimum. Tracer techniques and activation analysis are the most convenient methods for control of the purity and separation procedure.
3. It is very important to choose a target material of known and reproducible chemical composition and configuration to minimize control by each irradiation.

Nuclide production starts with the preparation of target material. The general requirements are more or less known and have been compiled in a comprehensive monograph;[27] further information and consideration will be restricted to conditions affecting primarily the purity of the target material. When sufficiently pure target material is not commercially available it is usual to carry out a purification work before irradiation. The following methods can be used: recrystalization, sublimation, distillation, electrolysis, and chromatographic methods. For simple irradiation conditions and irradiation of chemical stable samples such as metals, the target may be wrapped in aluminum foil of high purity before being placed in the aluminum can for irradiation.

To prevent unnecessary contamination or possible loss if volatile products are expected, the target material is closed or sealed in small plastic tubes or in high purity quartz ampule. Plastic ampule and plastic sample containers are particularly advantageous for short irradiations, since they do not acquire appreciable amounts of induced activity. However, in longer irradiations or in irradiations with high neutron flux, many plastics become brittle and tend to desintegrate. For such types of irradiations, mostly performed in central irradiation position, the target material is sealed into a quartz ampule and mounted in a special aluminum holder.

In addition to the straightforward reactions — direct reactions for example are (n,γ), (n,p), and (n,α) — it is possible to produce the radionuclides on the reactor by the secondary reactions. The emitted particle from the neutron-induced reaction interacts with some components present in irradiated target to give reactions like (x,n), (x,p), or (x,α), The radioactive product of the secondary reaction is after the irradiation separated from the target mixture. These types of production procedures based on the successive reactions require the development of the special irradiation devices.[23,24] For example, the reactor production of ^{18}F will be discussed. The first reaction — ^{6}Li (n,t) ^{4}He, which can also be written ^{6}Li $(n,^{4}He)$ ^{3}H has a cross-section of 950 barn for thermal neutrons and produces 2.73 MeV tritons and 2.05 MeV alpha-particles. The tritons are sufficiently energetic to initiate (t,p) and (t,n) reactions. This could be used for the production of ^{18}F using for irradiation the compounds containing enriched ^{6}Li and oxygen. The production processes reported[28,29] prefered effectively mixed lithium carbonate (sometimes are used also Li_2O, $Li(OH)_2$, or $LiAlO_2$). Lithium carbonate is advantageous because of its thermal stability, chemical purity, and good yields. A disadvantage of this production method is co-production of high amounts of tritium, which complicates the chemical separation of ^{18}F. The use of secondary reactions is limited on special cases as the yields from these processes are low.

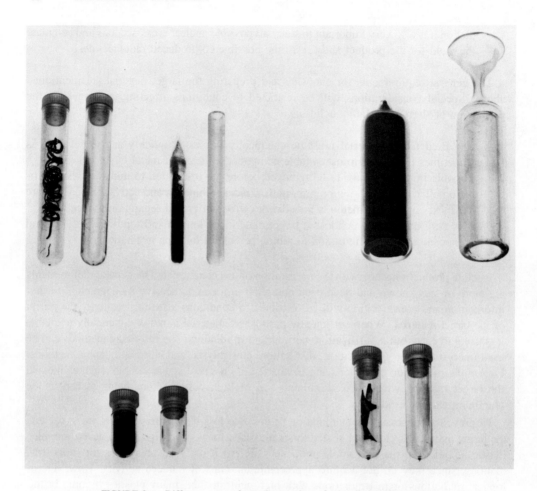

FIGURE 3a.   Different types of sample containers for irradiation in a reactor.

B. Irradiation Containers and Activation Loops

Target material holders — hardware of irradiation system — varies not only between different types of reactors, but varies also for different types of irradiation positions in the same reactor. In standard operating techniques the samples are irradiated in two types of containers: (1) sample containers, which cover the target material and protect it against surrounding. They are mostly plastic or quartz ampules. (b) Transport rabitts, the holder of sample containers. These containers are made mostly from high purity aluminum and enable insertion of samples into and remove them from the reactor core. Each transport container should hold more than one sample for irradiation. Figure 3 shows a typical sample container and transport container for insertion and irradiation in research TRIGA type reactors.[30]

Reactors used for the production of radionuclides have basically two different positions for irradiation. The first one is a fixed position in the reactor core, with the central irradiation position and couple of other positions in core. The second type of irradiation possibility is the mobile positions which are mostly used for short-time irradiations, experimental work, and activation analysis. On the TRIGA type reactors, there is a special irradiation system, the rotary specimen rack (called also ''lazy susan''). This rack is located around the core, rotates and provides the supplement facility for irradiation of about 40 samples in a uniform neutron flux. Rotation of the specimen rack eliminates flux variation from position to position in the reactor and permits equal irradiations of different samples with variations lower than 1 to 2%.

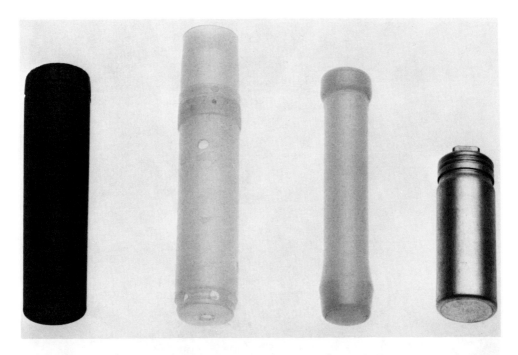

FIGURE 3b.   Examples of rabitts used for transportation of sample containers in hydraulic or pneumatic transport systems.

This ring also has a better cooling and a lower neutron flux, therefore the heating and radiation damage of irradiated samples is not a serious problem. Figure 4 shows the scheme of TRIGA reactor pool with a rotary specimen rack and transport system tubings.

Another type of activation in reactors involves the activation loop. It is a special assembly circulating gases, solutions, or molten salts, samples past the core of the reactor and then to a setup outside the reactor. This type of activation may be used for preparation of short-lived radionuclides in solution or in gas phase. A number of activation loops have been used for studying engineering aspects of reactor design, but only a few have been used for continuous radionuclide processing. As a practical example of the use of the activation loop in production of radionuclides, the production of ^{85m}Kr which can be used in the ventilation studies in medical diagnostic[31] can be mentioned.

C. Target Transfer Systems

By irradiation in low and moderate fluxes no special equipment will be required beyond that necessary to locate the targets in their proper irradiation positions. The irradiated target material should be delivered preferably from the reactor directly to the processing laboratory or in the manipulation hood without any packing and manual transfer. Short-term irradiations under well-defined conditions, as well as fast delivery of irradiated high active samples, are most conveniently achieved with the use of so-called rabitt systems and pneumatic or hydraulic tube facilities. Remote controlled systems are provided for loading and unloading of irradiation containers. Figure 5 shows schematically the general arrangement. It consists of three main parts: (1) the heavy shielded part outside the reactor for the sample transport system; (2) the load and unload mechanism and electronic equipment; and (3) the part inside the reactor with shielding and moderating material surrounding the sample transport tube.

There are many modifications of pneumatic tubes depending on the type of the reactor. One of the major advantages of the pneumatic tubes (air rabitt system) lies in the fact that

FIGURE 4. A view of the inside of the TRIGA II reactor. The tubing transport system and the ring (rotary specimen rack) can be seen. The ring slowly rotating around the core by irradiation is used in activation analysis experiments.

samples which are not watertight can be placed in reactor core; further advantage is a high velocity of transported samples, which is important for the preparation of short-lived radionuclides. A disadvantage could be the activation of argon (^{41}Ar with a half-life of 1.83 hr is produced) when air is used as a gas medium in pneumatic system. Several operating reactors have a hydraulic tube system to bring the samples on reproducible position or in the core and after irradiation back in the loading station. The time scale on which these tubes operate are the order of minutes in contrast to the few seconds for pneumatic system. The advantage of hydraulic system is a very low contamination of reactor ventilation system with co-produced ^{41}Ar activity.

The followed step by the reactor radionuclide production — processing of the target and chemistry — is done in a target processing facility — hot laboratory. Target chemistry or chemical processing of the irradiated target after bombardment is practically the same for reactor and cyclotron targets. The chemical separation methods used for purification of

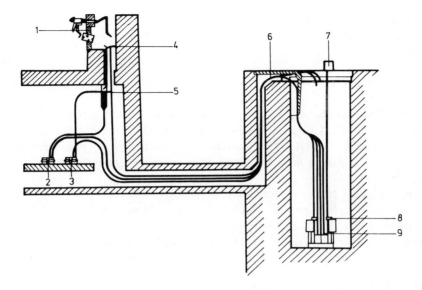

FIGURE 5. The general arrangement of the hydraulic target transport system on the Heidelberg TRIGA II reactor. (1) Loading cell with (4) loading station, (2) suction and (3) pressure pumps, (5) transport tubing system, (6) monitoring system, (7) position distributor, (8) rotary specimen rack, and (9) in-core irradiation positions.

radioactive product from target material and co-produced radioactive elements have the same basis. Special methods must be applicated for the fast separation procedures by preparation of short-lived radionuclides. Fast separation methods including modificated standard separation techniques, and in special cases are developed new modern separation techniques.[32] In general the following methods are used in separation: precipitation, distillation, volatilization, sublimation, solvent extraction, thermochromatographical separation, ion exchange, and other chromatographical methods. For separation and purification of short-lived radionuclides and labeled compounds two methods are prefered: ion exchange chromatography and high pressure liquid chromatography — HPLC.[33,34] More information and details about the processing of the target after the reactor irradiations may be found in Chapter 5 and for cyclotron radionuclides in Chapter 4.

D. Use of Enriched Target Material

Using enriched nuclide targets in production of radionuclides by the (n,γ) reaction increases remarkably specific activity of the required radionuclide and can essentially reduce isotopic radiocontaminants. Use of isotopically enriched target material could be of exceptional interest when the abundance of the target atoms in an element is lower than 50% particularly in those cases where valuable target material can be reclaimed and used. An example of this latter point would be the case where the irradiated target is used directly as a special source of radiation, or in a chemical system where it is not diluted with normal element mixture and can be chemically recovered. By the small research reactors it may not be feasible to raise the neutron flux, however, one can achieve the same result by using a separated isotope as target material in certain cases where the target isotope occurs in low natural abundance. In some cases of radionuclide production by (n,p) and (n,α) reactions, the use of separated isotope targets can be justified. It is desirable to obtain good recovery of enriched nuclides and use it repeatedly while these nuclides are usually very expensive. Sometimes for the enriched isotopes the term "separated isotopes", is used which could possibly better express the way of its origin, however, the word "separation" has in chemistry another signification. Enriched isotopes are commercially available from the following suppliers:

- Isotopes sales; Oak Ridge National Laboratory; P. O. Box X, Oak Ridge, Tennessee 37830, USA.
- Reactor Experiments Inc., 963 Terminal Way, San Carlos, California 94070, USA
- Isotec Inc., 7542 McEwen Rd., Centerville, Ohio 45459, USA.
- Rohstoff Einfuhr GmBH., 4000 Düsseldorf 1, Faunastrasse 61 West Germany.
- Soreq Nuclear Research Center; Israel Atomic Energy Commission, Yavne 70600, Israel
- Centre d'Etudes Nucléaires de Saclay; 91190 Gif-sur-Yvette.
- Stable isotopes; Monsanto Research Corporation, Mound facility — Stable Isotope Sales; P.O. Box 32, Miamisburg, Ohio 45342, USA.
- Ventron GmBH., Postfach 6540, D-7500 Karlsruhe, Germany (delivery of oxygen-stable isotopes only).

III. PARTICLE ACCELERATOR TARGETS

A. Introduction to Cyclotron Targetry

The second principal facility for the large scale of radionuclide production is the particle accelerator or cyclotron. Radionuclide production in a cyclotron requires the solution of a number of special problems. The three main problems are (1) to obtain beams of different particles of the required energy and intensity, (2) to design the target assemblies for irradiation of different materials, and (3) to find suitable nuclear reaction giving maximum isotope yield.

Particle accelerators are used for the studies of basic physical problems; for ion implantation; for the production of fast neutrons for therapy in oncology, and for material testing. However, the production of radionuclides for the medical use has been a major justification for continued operation and new construction of many cyclotrons in the world. In the last decade, there has been great interest on positron-emitting radionuclides such as ^{11}C, ^{13}N, and ^{15}O, which are used in medical and biological studies either in very simple chemical forms for direct clinical use, or converted into chemical intermediates or complicated biomolecules.

There are 51 accelerators[17] (from which are 49 cyclotrons) in the world dedicated to radionuclide production for medical use in or near the hospitals. The main scope of these machines, sometimes also called "medical cyclotron" or "compact cyclotron" is the preparation of short-lived radionuclides in very high-specific activities for direct use on the medical site. Both linear and circular accelerators consist in principle of three main parts: (1) ion source, (2) the accelerator section, and (3) the target. The target is that part of a cyclotron facility on which accelerated ions impinge to trigger off a nuclear reaction. The main purpose of the cyclotron target is to support the target material during irradiation and to protect the target material against overheating and evaporation in the vacuum of the machine.

In principle and construction, the reactor target and the reactor irradiation conditions are more simple compared to the cyclotron bombardment and cyclotron targets. In cyclotron bombardments the variety of possible targets and problems combined with target systems is so large that only a few generalities can be mentioned. The main emphasis in this part, however, will describe some general characteristics of the cyclotron target and give some details about the different target systems for routine radionuclide production developed and used in well-known cyclotron laboratories. Construction and manufacture of the target, choice of the material for the manufacture of the target and target holder, recovery of the activated target from the irradiation position to the laboratory, and use of enriched target materials and estimation of a suitable irradiation conditions for an optimum yield of appropriate radionuclide are topics to be covered in this part.

Cyclotron targets can sometimes be of very simple construction — especially if the target material is a high melting metal foil with a good heat conductivity and if the resulting radioactive product is not volatilized in vacuum. However, most target materials and practical irradiation conditions are far beyond these extreme good conditions and therefore most of the targets used for routine production of radionuclides are very complicated systems. Also from economical reasons, automatization of production procedure and remote handling control, the construction of the targets that do not require highly sophisticated technology would be of the aim of most cyclotron radionuclide production laboratories. For the majority of target systems it is difficult and sometimes impossible to realize these requirements with regards to the complicated irradiation conditions and used technology.

Though there are great differences in design and construction of cyclotron targets, there are some common conditions for all targets, which are being required by the physical characteristics of nuclear reaction and used target material. Important basic physical characteristics of desired nuclear reaction are the nuclear reaction cross-section, the stopping power of the bombarding particle in used target material and nature of the appropriate target material and reactivity of produced radioactive species. Just before planning and irradiation, these physical constants can be calculated, and some dimensions and important parameters for designing of the target defined. The optimum initial energy, total power imput in the target, and projectile energy optimum range in the target material could be defined and from the stopping power figures there can be defined the optimum thickness of the target material. If the gas is used as target material then it is possible to define the length and the diameter of the target and the pressure of the gaseous medium. Other parameters of the target should be estimated experimentally. These are, for example, material of the target holder, foils and foil cooling system, etc.

Generally, there are principal factors, experimentally verified,[35] which have to be taken into account when designing cyclotron target for radionuclide production:

1. The physical and chemical properties and purity of target material or potential use of enriched isotopes.
2. The selection of beam energy of bombarding particles that will maximize the yield of required radionuclide and minimize the co-production of possible impurities.
3. The beam current to be used, while overheating of the target material have to be taken into consideration. The principal problem in cyclotron irradiations is cooling, since the energy dissipation in the target can become quite large — of the order of few kW over a small area of square centimeter.
4. The method to be used to recover the radioactive material, either during the bombardment, which is mostly possible only by gaseous targets; or after bombardment.
5. The selection of suitable materials for construction of component parts of target holder system.
6. The provision of cooling adequate to ensure minimum temperature-rise of the beam entry foil window consistent with optimum temperature-rise of target material.
7. If possible, one would prefer to have in the target only atoms of the element that are concerned in the chosen reaction.

The design of cyclotron targets is primarily determined by the target material to be irradiated and consideration of the rate of production of the required radionuclide. In addition,

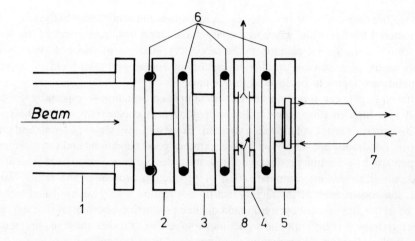

FIGURE 6.   Schematic view of the external target system. (1) Beam line, (2) collimator, (3) insulator, (4) double foil system, (5) target head, (6) O-ring system, (7) water cooling, and (8) He gas foil cooling.

the shape and size of the particle beam may be an important factor. Cost of the target material, which can be very high indeed, particularly if enriched material is used, also affects the final target design.

B. Target Types and Arrangements

In the first decades after the discovery of the cyclotron by E. O. Lawrence,[10] and first developments of radionuclide production procedures, some basic works had been published about cyclotron targets and target problems combined with radionuclide production.[36-40] There are practically no standard target equipment in this special research branch and there are also no commercial suppliers of target assemblies on the market, with the exception of two cyclotron producers — Cyclotron Corporation and CGR-Thompson — which can deliver simple targets with a machine, which in our experience has only a limited applicability. Because of broad diversity in the use of cyclotron targets and a variety of technical possibilities to solve the special problems in cyclotron target design, these targets are for the most part constructed and manufactured directly in the workshops of cyclotron laboratories.

Tight cooperation between the cyclotron physicist and operators, radiochemists, and precision mechanists by the construction of the new target system is advisable. The development of new sophisticated target systems and great progress in the last years in this field shows the published works from the different cyclotron laboratories.[41-44]

For a better understanding of target problems, Figure 6 shows a cross-sectional (schematical) view of common target assembly and important components composing the whole target system. Nevertheless, it must be said that in the practice each target must be adapted to the conditions of each particular experiment.

The entire simple target assembly shown in Figure 6 is attached to the end of the beam line. The collimator (made from aluminum, tantalum, or other materials) prevents beam from striking the beam line, electron suppressor ring, and O-ring support structure. By defocusing the beam on a small aperture a section of reasonably uniform power density is selected to fall on the target material. The beam profile behind the collimator should be, in diameter, smaller than the surface of the target material, so that the backing plate will not be irradiated. The beam should be homogen over the whole surface of the target material. It is very important to eliminate the beam hot spots which can cause local overheating of target material. The electron suppressor is used to prevent back-streaming of electrons from

FIGURE 7. Exploded view of the internal target head used on the Heidelberg compact cyclotron.

the target and enables exact measurements of the beam current. The foil system can be cooled by spraying the foils with pre-cooled helium gas or another gaseous medium. The advantage of helium is that no radioactive products are co-produced in the gas phase. The target backing plate is regularly cooled with water. The insulator makes the beam current measurements possible on the Faraday cup basis.

In the foregoing figure only the "external targets" have been illustrated, i.e., external are those targets installed outside the accelerator chamber and in which the target material is separated by the foil from the machine or beam line vacuum. An example of the other system, "internal target", is presented in Figure 7.

C. Classification of Cyclotron Targets

Cyclotron targets may be subdivided into different groups. The following survey of classifications of cyclotron targets may help to make some questions about the targets clearer. According to the use of the irradiated material, targets can be classified as follows:

1. Targets for the production of radionuclides. The first group, and probably the largest one, includes the typical production targets for the routine production of radionuclides for application in different research fields. Typical of this group is that the product is delivered mostly after physical or chemical separation from irradiated nonactive target material.
2. Targets which are themselves objects of investigation. The targets of the second group may include substances which are bombarded with particles in the cyclotron for the purpose of studying their physical properties. The use of these types of targets is limited exclusively to scientific investigation, for example, in nuclear physics studies.
3. Targets for production of other nucleons or targets for the generating of radiation. These targets are produced for the generating of radiation which are used for further investigation or for other purposes. This group includes for example, the titanium-tritium targets for the generating of neutrons. The use of these targets extends far beyond the purely scientific domain.

According to the state of aggregation of the irradiated target materials, targets are classified into three groups: (1) Solid and metal foil targets, (2) liquid targets and dissolved target material in a liquid medium, and (3) gaseous targets.

The majority of cyclotron targets used for radionuclide production are solid, either in the elemental form, usually as a metal foil, or a salt. For the preparation of solid targets, the target material with a relatively good physical and mechanical properties, especially with a high melting point should be used. As the range of the bombarding particles in solid state materials do not exceed several hundred microns, a relatively thin layer of the target material is sufficient to provide a "thick target". The metal foils, blocks, cylinder and thin films, pills or pressed tablets on an appropriate fundamental support are generally used as targets in this group. As a support for the target material aluminum or copper is used and the irradiated material is attached to the target backing plate by different methods. The important factor is a suitable cooling of the target material and a good heat conductivity between the target material and the backing plate. On the other hand, to show the great difference in the design of the targets it could be useful to let the target material melt by a dissipating power of the beam, which can help to recover the gaseous radioactive products from a solid target material; for example, the production and use of ^{11}C via the deuteron bombardment of B_2O_3.[45-47]

In the past a large number of methods[43-49] for the production of the medically important radionuclide ^{123}I have been reported. The ^{124}Te(p,2n) ^{123}I reaction is the most favorable method for production of ^{123}I at a low-energy cyclotron. This reaction has been studied by different groups[51-53] using ^{124}TeO$_2$ targets with various levels of enrichment. Different methods of separation, (mostly the sublimation technique is used) of ^{123}I activity from the ^{124}TeO$_2$ target were examined to determine the optimal conditions for recovery of radioactivity and recycling of target material. This perfectly developed production technique can be used as a representative for presentation of a common example of the solid target system.[54]

An exploded view of the target and target head used for the production of ^{123}I on the German Cancer Research Center in Heidelberg is shown in Figure 8.

Targets were prepared by melting the ^{124}TeO$_2$ (enrichment between 91.0 up to 96.0%) on a platinum backing plate and covering them with 6 μm "Havar" foil. The target was then placed in a shallow cavity in the target holder and directly cooled by pre-cooled silicon oil. The target can be rapidly attached to the beam line and is easily removed after bombardment. This target system is used many years for the three times a week routine production of ^{123}I and ^{121}I in our center. The same system can be used for many other production procedures, for example, for the production of ^{38}K.

Other target systems and more details about this production method have been published by the groups at BNL,[52,55] Milan,[51] Eindhoven,[53] and Julich. Karlsruhe group has developed the ^{123}I production via ^{124}Te(p,2n) ^{123}I reaction on a commercial basis,[54] using a target system involving direct contact of the cooling water with the ^{124}TeO$_2$ target material. The main disturbing radionuclidic impurity in ^{123}I produced via the ^{124}Te(p,2n) ^{123}I reaction on highly enriched ^{124}Te is ^{124}I (4.15 d).

The second suitable elaborated ^{123}I production process involves the ^{123}Xe-^{123}I generator method using ^{122}Te(^{3}He,2n) ^{123}Xe, and ^{122}Te(^{4}He,3n) ^{123}Xe→^{123}I reactions. An advantage of the generator method is the higher purity, although there are some difficulties with the reproducibility of the recovery of ^{123}Xe from the target material.[50,56,57] The target systems used for the recovery of ^{123}Xe from the irradiated ^{124}TeO$_2$ is shown in Figure 9.

Cyclotrons with high energy protons (about 60 MeV) can produce ^{123}I via the ^{127}I(p,5n) ^{123}Xe→^{123}I reaction.[58] The main drawback of this method is the complicated design and construction of the target, first for the aggressive target material used (iodine or iodine compounds); second for the high power dissipation in the target system. On the other hand the very low price of the target material and the highest purity of the ^{123}I product is advantageous.

There are two reasons for using liquid targets. The first one is that the water or another liquid material is a proper target material. For example the water is used as target material for the production of ^{13}N via ^{16}O(p,^{4}He) ^{13}N reaction. The second reason is connection with

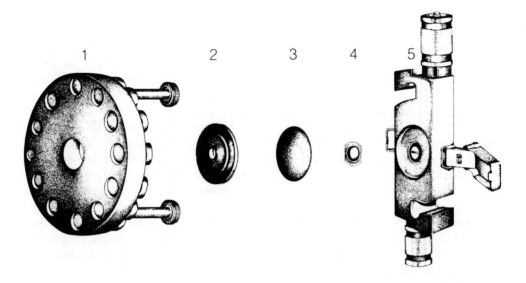

FIGURE 8. Exploded view of the external target used for irradiations of solid compounds melted in platinum cavity, (1) Flange, (2) foil holder, (3) "Havar" foil, (4) Pt. backing with melted $^{124}TeO_2$, (5) target holder.

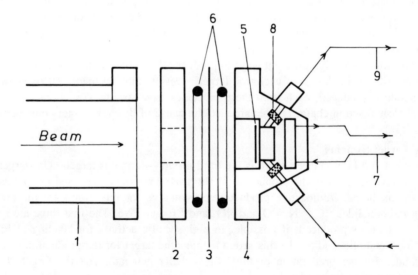

FIGURE 9. Scheme of the target system for the extraction gaseous products from solid mattrix. (1) Beam line, (2) collimator, (3) insulator, (4) target head, (5) foil, (6) O-ring system, (7) water cooling, (8) sintered stainless steel filters, (9) sweeping gas (He).

the subsequent chemical separation. By the production of short-lived radionuclides[59,60] the handling of the target and chemical processing must be undertaken as soon after bombardment as possible. Since the targets are very active immediately after bombardment, a considerable radiation hazard for personnel is involved. It could be minimized, if initial stages of the chemical separation procedure could be carried out either by remote handling or automatic system. The first phases of chemical operation are already complete if the target material is initially in solution. The irradiated solution after irradiation can be pumped out from the liquid target into a hot cell in order to make further chemical steps. Transport of the irradiated liquid material in the chemical laboratory can be completed while the cyclotron can irradiate another target and cyclotron room must not be opened.

If the water is used as the solvent for irradiation of salt solutions, then in such systems problems may rise up connected with the occurrence of radiolytically induced reactions not observed by irradiations of solid targets. If the water is irradiated with high beam currents, radiolysis gives rise to hydrogen and oxygen which have to be recombined with the aid of a catalyst (on Pd basis) and so prevent inexcessive rise in the pressure in the target.[61] Target material in liquid targets is enclosed in an appropriate container and separated from the beam line vacuum by a foil system. Two foils provide better protection for a cyclotron beam line vacuum in case of window failure. The foils are cooled with a pre-cooled helium gas, which helps to prolong the life of the foils. Also the recirculating of the irradiated medium or using a reciprocter can have a positive effect on the life of the foils and enables the use of higher beam currents. In the intensive routine production of radionuclides, could be after bombardment detected by γ-spectrometry radioactivity produced from the foil and recoiled in the irradiated solution.[62]

A typical example of the liquid target system used in routine production of ^{18}F is described by Clark.[61] This external target system for the production of ^{18}F via ^{16}O(^{4}He,pn) ^{18}F reaction has been successfully used for the production of high amounts of ^{18}F in water solution. The "loop" internal target system using the same nuclear reaction has been described by Lindner.[63] The produced ^{18}F was trapped on anion exchange resin situated in a column in a bypass of the "loop". Circulating water is used at first as the target material, but it has the second function of cooling medium. This type of irradiation needs a really good cooling. In our laboratory there has been developed target system for the production of high amounts of ^{13}N using water as the target medium. Figure 10 shows the arrangement of this system. After irradiation the water with ^{13}N was removed from the target and converted into ^{13}NH$_3$ form. All operations are remotely controlled.

Table 5 summarizes five different ways to produce ^{18}F in order to demonstrate the variety and complexity of the design of cyclotron targets. Despite the fact that in all five cases the same nuclide is produced, each from these processes have specific conditions. These particular nuclear reaction characteristics are also the cause of different target constructions.

D. Gas Target Systems

After solid and liquid targets there is the third group — gaseous targets. Gas targets are especially advantageous in the production of short-lived radionuclides used in applications in nuclear medicine. Radioactive products representative for this group are the positron emitting radionuclides ^{11}C, ^{13}N, ^{14}O and ^{15}O, and ^{18}F and ^{19}Ne. The first three are typical biological elements produced, if possible, in high-specific activity for labeling of biomolecules for metabolic studies. To this group belongs the target for the production of parent radionuclides for the preparation of the ^{81}Rb - $^{81}\Sigma$Kr generator and the targets for the generation of fast neutrons.[64,65]

Gas targets fall into two classes — those in which a gas is the target material and those in which target material is solid, but the produced activity is gaseous and can be removed from the target by sweeping gas.

As a typical example for the combination, gaseous target material and gaseous product radionuclide can be shown the production of ^{11}C over ^{14}N(p,^{4}He)^{11}C reaction.[66] Using a water-cooled, high pressure target, it can be radioactive product — ^{11}C — in a simple chemical form[67] swept out from the target with a target gas. Another example of such combinations are the production reactions ^{14}N(d,n)^{15}O, ^{18}O(p,n)^{18}F, and others.[42] A special case could be presented by the combination where the target material is a gas and the product is solid. Production of ^{81}Rb via the ^{82}Kr(p,2n)^{81}Rb reaction and ^{42}K via the ^{40}Ar(^{4}He,pn) ^{42}K represents this type of combination and hereby the type of target. Some of the target gases which are not expensive can be irradiated in a very simple target box. Such a target

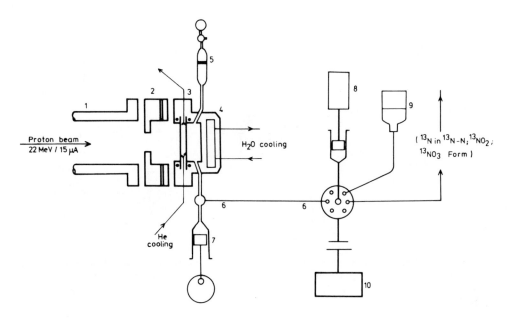

FIGURE 10. External liquid target system for the production of ^{13}N via the ^{16}O(p,α)^{13}N reaction using water as a target material. (1) Beam line, (2) collimator, insulator, (3) double foil system, (4) target body with target cavity, (5) volume compensation vessel, (6) remotely operated valves, (7) reciprocating pump, (8) injection pump, (9) target sterile water, (10) remote handling control system.

Table 5
^{18}F CYCLOTRON PRODUCTION METHODS

Nuclear reaction	Target material	Q-value (MeV)	Yield (mCi/μAh)	Target used[120]
^{20}Ne(d,α)^{18}F	Ne gas (99.99%)	2.796	23.80	External gas target
^{20}Ne(^{3}He,αp)^{18}F	Ne gas (99.99%)	-2.697^a	7.80	External gas target
(^{3}He,αn)^{18}Ne 1.67 s ^{18}F		-7.296		
^{16}O(^{3}He,p)^{18}F	O$_2$; Al$_2$O$_3$; H$_2$O	2.003^b		External targets and
(^{3}He,n)^{18}Ne 1.67 s ^{18}F		-3.196	6.70	int. water target
^{16}O(α,pn)^{18}F	O$_2$; Al$_2$O$_3$; Ta$_2$O$_5$	-18.544		Not studied, the energy of α
(α,2n)^{18}Ne 1.67 s ^{18}F	and H$_2$O	-23.773		is too low for this reaction
^{18}O(p,n)^{18}F	enriched ^{18}O (50 and 90% enrichment)	-2.400	6.5	External recirculating on Ag/CsOH target system

a   Yield is the sum of yields of both reactions.
b   Yield determined only for internal irradiation of water.

system consists of a cylindrical target box (made from stainless steel or aluminum) connected to a gas circulating system and fitted with a beam entry window. When the target gas is expensive (for example, Kr, enriched Kr isotopes ^{82}Kr, or ^{80}Kr used in some laboratories) and only a small quantity is available, the special construction with an excellent cooling facility for the foil entry window and target box must be guaranteed. As a safety precaution the target box is fitted to the trap with a molecular sieve (and cooled by liquid air) into which the gas can be withdrawn after irradiation (or in the case of the foil failure or other

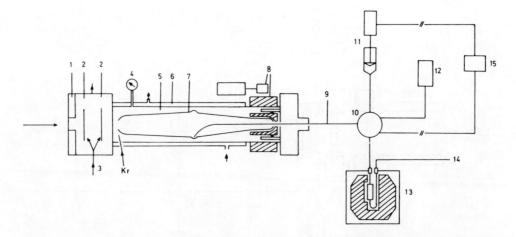

FIGURE 11a.   Scheme of ^{81}Rb production system. (1) Collimator, (2) foils, (3) foil cooling, (4) pressure gauge, (5) target body, (6) water cooling, (7) quartz liner, (8) magnetic rotation system, (9) solvent line, (10) remote operated valve, (11) injection pump, (12) reservoir with sterile water, (13) ^{81}Rb-^{81}Σ Kr generator, (14) waste, (15) electronic control.

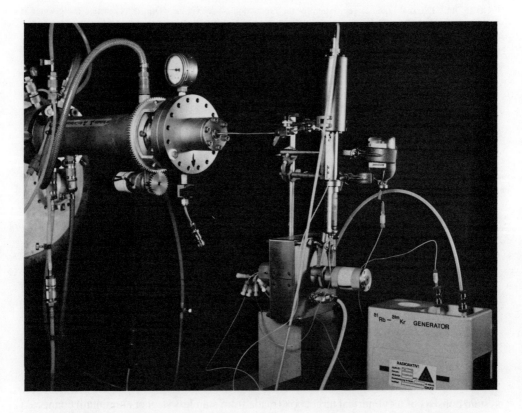

FIGURE 11b. ^{81}Rb production target system. Realization of the scheme shown on Figure 11a.

accident). The activity deposited on the walls inside the target or on the internal liner can be washed out and collected. After drying and evacuating the target box, gas can be released into the target by heating the molecular sieve. The irradiation may then be repeated. The target construction used natural Krypton gas as the target material (Figure 11).

This target construction used for the routine production of ^{81}Rb is a modified version of the target used for a number of years for the production of ^{18}F. The present design is remotely controlled and the target consists of a quartz liner inside a cylindrical stainless steel vessel. The quartz liner is connected to a rotor which was coupled magnetically to an external multipole magnet. By mechanical rotation of the external multipole magnet, the quartz liner is rotated allowing the inner surface of the liner to be washed by a solvent. Many other target designs for the production of ^{81}Rb have been reported.[44,68,69]

The second class of the gas targets, where the target material is solid and the produced activity is in a gas form, can be represented by two examples used in a routine production. Both have been developed by the Hammersmith group. The first is the production of ^{11}C via ^{11}B(d,2n)^{11}C reaction.[60,35] As target material is used bortrioxid spread on a stopped wedge inserted in the target box. Carrier gas (He) removes the activity from the target box which can be trapped in the storage system. The second example for this class of targets is the production of ^{13}N via the ^{12}C(d,n)^{13}N reaction, using activated charcoal as the target material. Carrier gas, in this case argon, flows over activated charcoal. These production methods have a great deal of difficulties, therefore many laboratories switched by the production of ^{11}C and ^{13}N on gas targets using gaseous target material. The gaseous rather than solid targets offer several advantages:

1.   The target design is more simple than by solid targets.
2.   There is no destruction of the target after the irradiation and no transport problems with the irradiated target.
3.   It is possible to adapt the range of absorbed energy in the irradiated target material to decrease or avoid the contaminating reactions and to optimize the yield of the appropriate radionuclide.

If the gas is used as the target material and the gaseous radioactive species are produced, three different ways can be used for removing the activity from the target box:

Open, or flow system — Produced radioactivity is continually removed at the appropriate flow rate from the target. An example is the production of ^{11}C via ^{14}N(p,^{4}He) ^{11}C reaction, where 600 cm^3/min has been found in our arrangement as the optimum flow rate for further operations. The flow rate is regulated automatically by a control valve. To maintain the pressure in the target at optimum (11 bar), the target is continually filled out with a new target gas from the gas cylinder. The target has an internal volume 130 cm^3 and the incident energy of protons of 14.8 MeV is absorbed in the 11 bar of nitrogen up to 2.9 MeV, which is Q-value for used nuclear reaction. Total volume of the target by the pressure of 11 bar is 1430 cm^3. To produce 1.5 Ci of ^{11}C and above-mentioned flow rate of target gas is the total volume of the nitrogen used 30000 cm^3. Even if 99.9995% purity of nitrogen is used, there is still a sufficient amount of CO/CO$_2$ — 0.1 vpm and carbohydrates, CH$_4$ — 0.1 vpm. Using the flow system, the great volume of the target nitrogen increases essentially the content of nonactive carbon. For the above-mentioned purity and total amount of 30000 cm^3 in the product would be 5.89 µg CO/CO$_2$ and 2.14 µg CH$_4$. The inactive carbon atoms decrease the specific activity of the ^{11}C product. To increase the specific activity of the product it is possible to use the stopped flow system.

Stopped flow system — By this procedure the target box is filled with the target gas. In our arrangement the target volume by 11 bar is 1430 cm^3. When the irradiation is completed, in comparison with the flow system it produced the same amount of activity, 1.5Ci, the gas is removed by the flow rate of 600 cm^3/min. In this target volume the amount of nonactive carbon atoms is about 20 times lower than it was in the first procedure. The using of the first or the second method of producing radioactive gases depends more or less on the application and further chemical processing of the product. If the ^{11}C in the form of ^{11}CO$_2$

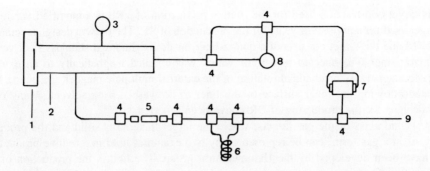

FIGURE 12a.   Gas recirculating target system. (1) Foil, (2) stainless steel target chamber, (3) pressure gauge, (4) three-way valves, (5) ^{18}F adsorption trap, (6) ^{18}O recovery trap, (7) pump, (8) flow meter, (9) vacuum.

or another simple form is applicated, the open flow system is used. For the complicated synthetic procedure the stopped flow system is preferred. The third possibility of removing of the activity from the gas targets is the closed circuit system.

Closed circuit system — In such systems the target — sweeping gas is recirculated in a closed system — ''loop'' and the produced activity could be either maximized and removed on the end of the bombardment, or can be removed continually by the bombardment over a trap fitted in a by-pass in the ''loop''. A typical example for the practical use of this sytem is ^{18}F production via the ^{18}O(p,n) ^{18}F shown schematically in Figure 12. With an advantage are the closed circuit systems applicated by the irradiation of expensive enriched target gases; or in cases where the radioactive product can react directly by irradiation in the trap to produce continuously intermediate product.

The parameters affecting the total yield recovered from the gaseous target may be divided into those affecting the activity within the gas target:

1.   Target material nuclear cross-section.
2.   Beam current. The maximum beam current in the gas target is determined by two factors. The first one is the pressure of appropriate gas target material in the system. It is desirable that the beam is completely attenuated before it reaches the back of the target. The second factor is the temperature of the irradiated gas. The density of the gas decreased with increased temperature of the irradiated gas, which leads to local dilution of the target gas and lower yields and irradiation of the back of the target chamber.
3.   Beam energy. Incident beam energy and the energy range of the particle in the target should be closely adapting to the cross-section curve of irradiated element. So it is possible to decrease or to avoid the contaminating reaction
4.   Target material thickness.
5.   Cooling of the target material.

Parameters affecting the recovery of the radioactivity from the target:

1.   Beam distribution
2.   Target material temperature
3.   Sweep gas flow rate
4.   Sweep gas composition and water content

A lot of published data are available describing the studies and behavior of the gas targets.

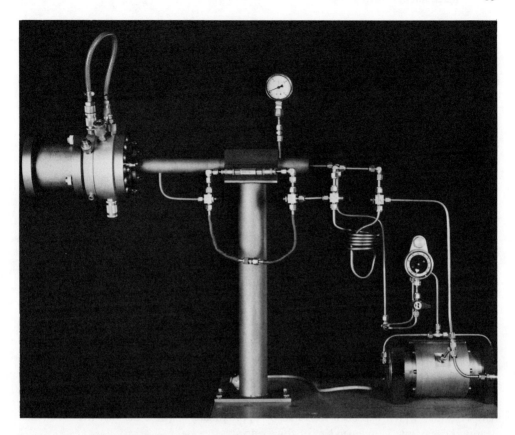

FIGURE 12b. Recirculating target system used for the production of anhydrous ^{18}F via the $^{18}O(p,n)^{18}F$ reaction. Realization of the scheme is shown on Figure 12a.

Oselka[70] has shown that the yields of radionuclides produced on gaseous targets were not proportional to the beam current or gas pressure. Their investigation has shown that for all currents greater than 1 μA the number of ionized molecules in the beam volume is essentially independent of external pressure and reaches plateau between 5 and 10 μA of beam current. They conclude that for the following reasons — plasma pressure, high temperature or electrical repulsion — the gas molecules are forced out of the beam in a fashion proportionate to beam current. The same effect has been observed by McDaniels[71] who has investigated the corrections for the change in density of molecules in gas targets as a function of beam current. This correction is often important in the determination of absolute cross-sections using a gas target. They have found that the dominant physical mechanism responsible for decrease in density of target gas atoms is just that of an overheating of the target gas chamber, rather than pulse or gradient effects. It is known from other sources[72] that for a beam of radius ''b'' and a gas target radius ''a'', the temperature difference between the center core and outer surface is defined by the equation:

$$\Delta T = \frac{dQ \ln (a/b)}{dt\ 2\pi\ LK}$$

where dQ/dt is the heat/sec warming the core of the target; L is the target length and K is the thermal conductivity of the irradiated gas.

From above-mentioned reasons it follows that the excellent cooling of the gas targets is of extreme importance.

The yield of the short-lived radionuclides in the target is defined very simply and will be described in detail in the next chapter. The yield of the gaseous product at the site of delivery, sometimes on the relatively longer distance may be affected by the half-life of the product. Many authors have investigated the optimal conditions of the flow rate, volume of the target chamber, length of the gas-carrying line (tubing system), and the diameter of the tubing. The optimum conditions for the flow rate giving a maximum yield has been studied by a Liege cyclotron group.[73,74] The authors described the formula for a flow rate D, which gives the maximum yield of production

$$D = \tfrac{1}{2}[\lambda V_r + (\lambda^2 V_r^2 + 4\,\lambda^2 V_r V_c)]$$

where, λ = decay constant of the produced radionuclide; V_c = the volume of the gas target; V_r = the inner volume of the gas-carrying line. They extended this mathematical expression about a supplementary hypothesis which takes into account the inhomogeneity of produced activity in the target chamber. Fills[75] reported about the flow system for the activation of gaseous or liquid samples. Based on the Hagen-Poisseuille principle

$$\frac{dV}{dt} = \frac{\pi\, r^4\, p}{8\,\eta\, 1}$$

where, dV/dt is a flow rate, r = inner diameter of tubing, η = dynamical viscosity which depends on temperature, and 1 is the length of the tubing. Through r^4 the consideration about the diameter of the used tubing is very important. They have investigated the optimum transport time, which has been found to be approximately 3/4 of the half-life when the measured decay rate is independent of flow velocity.

The dependence of the transit times of produced radioactive gases on the drive pressure was experimentally investigated by Hichwa.[76] The investigation has been done for the tuned conditions and compared with theoretical calculations for a gas model ^{15}O and gas flow through capillaries for a long distance between the cyclotron and medical site. The production rate is fixed by the beam energy and used beam current. After several half-lives the production of short-lived radionuclides is matched by their decay.

Development in the last few years shows a significant movement towards cyclotron and generator-produced short-lived positron emitting radionuclides. Many problems are common for the production of all short-lived radionuclides as for example the optimal irradiation conditions for a highest yield and high-specific activity, fast transport times, and corresponding synthesis times. However, it is therefore necessary to study the basic problems in this field in order to minimize those problems in the design of new target systems.

With respect to the irradiation position, the cyclotron targets can be arranged by bombardment internally or externally. The arrangement is governed by the type of accelerator facility, by the scientific or radionuclide commercial production program, by the characteristics of the target material, and by the used beam currents and cooling possibilities.

E. Internal and External Targets

The internal target arrangement is used as a rule for the targets, which are temperature, vacuum, and radiation resistant while they have to be suitable for operating directly inside the cyclotron vacuum chamber. By internal irradiations are samples irradiated in a high vacuum (of 10^{-5} to 10^{-6} mmHg). Therefore the targets irradiated internally must have a high work function in order that they cannot be evaporated when heated in the vacuum. Metals and compounds with low melting points cannot be used as internal targets (for example Zn,

Table 6
HEAT CONDUCTIVITY OF SOME
MATERIALS USED IN CONSTRUCTION
OF CYCLOTRON TARGETS AND FOILS

Material	Temperature (°C)	Heat conductivity ($cal/cm^{-1} \cdot sec \cdot C \cdot grad^{-1}$)
Al	18	0.504
Ag	18	0.992
Au	18	0.700
Mo	18	0.346
Ni	18	0.142
Pt	18	0.166
Stainless steel	18	0.115
Ti	50	0.037
Glas	20	0.002
Quartz	20	0.030

Heat conductivity of gases used as cooling medium.

N_2	0 (1 bar)	$57.36 \ 10^{-6}$
He	0 (1 bar)	$348.00 \ 10^{-6}$

Note: Giving the quantity of heat in calories which is trans-
mitted per second through a material 1 cm thick across
an area of square centimeter when the temperature difference is one degree Centrigrade.

Te, etc.). Internal targets are usually metal foils or blocks, mounted or melted in a good thermal contact on the intensively cooled backing plates. As material for backing plates construction — the target holder — it is important to choose the materials with a good heat conductivity. The heat conductivities of metals such as zirconium, titanium, tantalum, etc., are not the best, but are sufficient to allow the irradiation to be carried internally. Where the irradiated material is too expensive, and where high beam currents are used, or where the heat conductivity of the target material is poor, it is advisable to use more stable backing plate materials. Silver, copper, and aluminum have sufficiently high heat conductivity to be satisfactory as backing plates, however, the silver is practically unacceptable with regard to the price. The aluminum is by far the best material for the construction of target holders, as the price is acceptable and the amount of co-produced contaminants are very low. Table 6 shows the heat conductivities of important materials used in the construction of targets.

It is impossible to defocus the beam spot by internal irradiations to avoid destructive heating of the target material. The beam is concentrated on a very small surface and a considerable amount of power must be transferred from the target holder body into the cooling medium, as the cooling medium is mostly used in fast flowing water. To make the beam spot on the target material greater, the grazing incidence principle is used to reduce heat flux to a manageable level. Hence it follows that the basic problem of designing and construction of internal targets is dissipating the high power density of the internal beam. Solving this problem results in a higher yield of appropriate radionuclide in a shorter irradiation period.

At a small compact cyclotron (max. 22 MeV proton energy), it is easily possible by internal irradiation to make a beam current of 200 μA. The power density on a beam spot of 8 × 4 mm dimensions under these conditions on the target has a surface of 13.75 kW when all energy is stopped in the target. While the target material must be kept below the temperature at which either the target material or the radioactive product of the nuclear reaction could be evaporated, all the power from irradiated spot and target holder must be transferred into cooling water. Water cooling of the target has some limits given by heat conductivity of the target material and heat conductivity of the target holder on one side and vapor pressure and melting point of both on the other side. Also if the best target holder materials are used (for example Al or Cu); the thickness of the target material, thickness of backing plate, the pressure, and the flow rate of cooling water play very important factors by transferring the beam power from the target system. Vonberg[35] has experimentally determined that the maximum power which can be removed by water cooling under conditions of surface boiling is only about 4.5 kW/cm^2. The simple internal target, in a U-form curved copper tube, cooled intensive by water, does not allow the use of beam currents higher then about 50 to 60 µA of 40 MeV deuterons without melting. The construction of internal targets with different shapes, movable irradiated parts, and targets with sophisticated cooling systems were designed to spread the beam over a large area with resultant better heat dissipiation. Martin[77] has described a technically complicated internal target system where the target material is sealed within a thin-walled aluminum tube which is mounted concentrically within a slightly larger thin-walled tube. Cooling is provided by water flowing at high velocity in the anulus between both tubes. The analogous target system has been described by Wieland[42] for the production of gaseous positron emitting radionuclides using an enriched target material and internal target system. It is extremely difficult to design and construct the internal targets for irradiation of liquids or gaseous target materials. The target system used in the Oak Ridge laboratory have solved this problem. Another internal target system used for a long time in the routine production of ^{123}I has been developed by Schulz and Belleman.[78] The target material enriched ^{124}TeO$_2$ is cooled directly by cooling water and closed against the machine vacuum by the Cu(Be) foil. For the internal irradiations many other special irradiation devices have been designed.[79-81] Such sophisticated arrangements are technologically very complicated and expensive in construction, therefore further development of such systems was abandoned in many laboratories.

Following bombardment, the internal target can be removed automatically, if possible, from the vacuum chamber and carried with a transfer system out of the cyclotron room and deposited behind lead shielding to await chemical processing. Not only the target material, but practically all components of the target holder become radioactive to greater or lesser extent.

Larger installations and commercial producers of radionuclides have developed a special assembly for internal irradiations. This facility consists of: (1) rabitt system for the transporting of the target holder from and to the cyclotron room, (2) target loading cell, in which target holder can be preevacuated before it is loaded into the cyclotron vacuum chamber, (3) hydraulic system, for the introduction of the target holder in the proper position in the cyclotron and withdrawing it on the end of the bombardment.

After the bombardment the target materials are removed from the target holder and processed in the chemical hot laboratory.

Internal targets have a limited application. The cyclotron targets for radionuclide production and for other purposes are mostly positioned outside the cyclotron vacuum chamber and are known as "external targets". The accelerated particles are extracted by an electrostatic deflector into a beam transport system. The external beam transport system consists of one switching magnet for the deflection of the beam in two or more beam lines. The extracted beam is defocused by quadrupole magnets and is collimated by the apperture — collimator — which diameter is slightly smaller than the surface of the target material. The diameter of the collimator depends on the distance between the collimator and the surface of the target material. The target material is separate from the vacuum of the beam line by thin foil or by system of foils.[82] Figure 13 shows the double foil system used in our laboratory.

The target spot of about 20 mm in diameter is sufficient. The beam spot should not shift

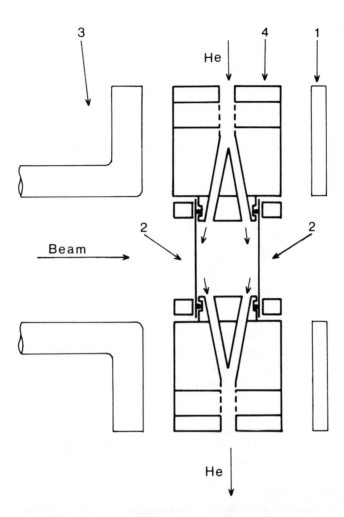

FIGURE 13. Double foil system enables intensive cooling of both foils by pre-cooled helium gas. (1) Insulator, (2) foils, (3) beam line, (4) aluminum foil holder.

more than 7 mm in position during irradiation. The great advantage of external target irradiations is that the target material can be hit by defocused beam on the whole surface which is larger than the irradiated surface by internal irradiations. To avoid the influence of "hot spots" (nonhomogeneity of the particles in the beam profile) in the beam and herewith the local overheating and evaporation of the target material, it is advisable to oscilate with a beam by the irradiation. A section of a reasonably uniform power density λ is so selected to fall on the target. One of the important factors which may influence the target design is a beam broadening. Foils separate the constituent parts of the target, but they must transmit radiation. An initially collimated beam may broaden because of numerous collisions of its particles. The consequences of beam broadening may be either positive, while it makes the radiation act over a wide region (gives a better cooling possibility); or negative, to decrease in intensity of the directed beam. The most probable deflection angle depends on basic experimental parameters. In our consideration we took into account not only one particle, but the beam as a whole. Hence, we are dealing with a mean value.

1.   λ is proportional to the square root of the foil thickness. This dependence follows from statistics.
2.   λ is inversely proportional to the particle energy E, which follows from the most elementary properties of deflections.
3.   λ is proportional to the charge of the nucleus Z, which follows from the properties of elastic collisions.

According to the above, the following relation approximately holds for, in nonrelativistic case:

$$\lambda \approx Z \sqrt{\frac{d}{E}}$$

For more information about this problem see References 121 and 122. Most irradiations on the external targets are carried out at beam currents of 5 to 50 μA.

The following examples show the fields where the use of external targets is advantageous:

1.   In exact measurements in nuclear physics experiments[87,88]
2.   In activation analysis with accelerated particles[89,96]
3.   In production of radionuclides where the gases, low melted salts, and material that need careful treatment, are irradiated[44,59]
4.   For production of short-lived radionuclides produced and used directly at location of the cyclotron[41,90]
5.   For activations where radioactive product is thermally or radiative sensitive and nonstabile[91,92]
6.   For all studies performed locally — on the beam stop — where the time of removing and transportation of the target may be too long, or dangerous[93-95]

F. Foils and System of Foils
   The main reason for the use of the entry foil window is to protect the target material and isolate it from the vacuum of the machine. Foils are very important parts of practically all targets. With the exception of the foils used for the degradation of the particle energy on the required incident reaction energy — so-called beam degrading filters — all other foils are very thin, in the order of 1 to 50 μm. Generally, for the preparation of the foils metals with excellent mechanical characteristics, good heat conductivity, and a high melting point are preferred. The power dissipated on the foil depends on the material and thickness of the used foil, and can be easily calculated.[83] The following metals are successfully used for the preparation of the foils: Al, Cu, Cu(Be) alloys, stainless steel, Ti, Ni, W, Mo, Havar,[84] and some other alloys. Aluminum is preferred whenever possible, as other metals might produce after a longer period of irradiation quite a high amount of different contaminants; for example, deuteron or proton irradiation of Cu foils producing long-lived ^{65}Zn ($T_{1/2}$ = 243.8 d); and ^4He and ^3He irradiation producing ^{67}Ga ($T_{1/2}$ = 78.3 h). A disadvantage in some applications of aluminum foils is its lack of strength. During the bombardment with a higher beam current the pressure in the target may rise, which could result in a distortion or even fracture of the foil. Schulz[78] investigated the beam intensity limitations of foils from different metals; Cu, Pt, Ta, Ag, Cu(Be), and W. The foils were tested by irradiation with a 40 MeV deuteron beam and a beam current up to 100 μA. From all the tested materials, the best one was reported to be Cu or Cu(Be) alloy foil. The disadvantage of copper was the oxidation with water by irradiation conditions due to elevated temperature and radiation effects. The life time of Cu foils has been found to be about 1000 μAh. Tungsten foils of

50 μm thicknesses were found very good, but mechanical characteristics are very poor. It is difficult to locate a manufacturer willing to make pin-hole free tungsten foils less than 10 μm thick. Using different methods, other authors[65] tested the metal foils from Ni, Mo, W, and Havar. They found that the foils developed two different types of leaks. The first one was a slow permanent leak, rising from a small pin-hole melted through the foil; the second type was attributed to gas diffusing through the hot foil. The pressure capability tests showed that increased thickness allowed operation of higher pressures. On the other hand, it was found that maximum beam intensity is inversely proportional to the foil thickness. Thus, if a high pressure operation is necessary, a compromise between increased thickness for more pressure and decreased thickness for more beam intensity is necessary. These results agree with our experiments and with other published works.

In recent years "Havar" foils* have often been used in nuclear physics and in the construction of radionuclide gas targets as entry or exit window foils. Havar foil is a high tensile strength cobalt-based alloy composed from seven metals: Co (42.5%), Cr (20.0%), Fe (17.46%), Ni (13.0%), W (2.8%), Mo (2.4%), Mn (1.6%), and small amounts of C (0.2%) and Be (0.04%).[85] In our laboratory we use Havar foils in three different thicknesses (6 μm; 12 μm, and 22 μm thicknesses) as entry windows on gas targets for the production of ^{81}Rb and ^{18}F and on the liquid target for ^{13}N production. To extend the life of the foil, two foil system have been developed. Figure 13 shows the two foil system cooled with a pre-cooled helium gas, which is flowing in the space between both foils. This sandwich foil system has been used with success in practice by the irradiation with a 22 MeV proton beam current up to 20 μA. The foils are controlled or changed, when necessary, after about 1000 μAh.

Foils are usually made tight on the target support with O-ring seals. The material of O-rings is perbunan, viton, indium metal, copper, or sometimes gold. When the assembly is tightened together, the O-rings are compressed so that metal-to-metal contact of the foil with flange (supporting structure) is obtained. To solder the foil to the support, the conductive cooling of the foil will be superior to the O-ring method. However, there are two difficulties; one, the mechanical problem of soldering a thin foil on a robust support; and secondly, the solder joints can have a tendency to tear the foil. By the thin foils, use of the O-rings is therefore preferred. The choosing of different O-ring materials depends on the temperature, which they withstand. For extreme conditons metal O-rings are used.

G. Arrangement of the Target in Irradiation Facility

There are many different possibilities of arrangements of the external targets on the cyclotron irradiation facility. The main purposes of this facility could be commercial production of radionuclides or production of short-lived radionuclides direct in medical centers, or combined nuclear physics experimental studies with radionuclide co-production. These activities could represent some different basic aims of cyclotron laboratories. Possible arrangements, which vary from one facility to another, of the allocation of external target systems in the Heidelberg cyclotron laboratory are shown in Figure 14. Other examples of target arrangements can be found elsewhere.[41,107]

There are six beam lines with targets arranged as terminal closures. Utilizing one beam line for the irradiation of more targets in tandem system is shown on beam line No. 3. One target device for irradiation of solid targets in vacuum, can be situated in the middle part of the beam line.[41] Generally, the second target is then located on the end of the same beam line as the beam stop. This target can be used for the production of long-lived activities, which could be built up for a long period without additional beam-on-target time. If possible, in routine production of high activities a permanent irradiation position should be reserved

---

* Obtained from "Hamilton Precision Metals", Lancaster, Pa., USA.

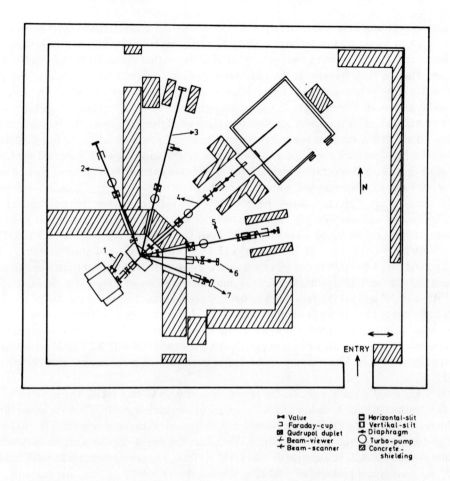

FIGURE 14.   Cyclotron irradiation facility. For example, the Heidleberg cyclotron laboratory with AEG compact cyclotron is shown.

for target systems used many times; the reasons being possible contamination risk by the production of high amount of activity should be limited on one small place; and the fact that the radioactivity of the whole target production system is increasing with every following irradiation. A carriage way system for the transport of irradiated targets to the hot laboratory is situated on the beam line No. 5. Gas targets with gas transport tubing system, which allow the transfer of the gaseous produced radioactivity out of the cyclotron room, are situated on the beam lines No. 6 and 7. Beam line No. 4 is used for the production of fast neutrons and No. 2 for radiobiological experiments.

There are two other ways of improving the production of cyclotron radionuclides. Both are shown in Figure 15.

First is the proposal from the Cyclotron Unit group,[86] (shown in Figure 15 left) that a full power of the beam should be ''split'' so that the irradiation of two or more external targets simultaneously will be possible. The scanning magnet switches an effective beam over more targets only as high as can safely be tolerated. This would seem to offer considerable advantages — to make the irradiations and production of longer-lived radionuclides more effective and economical. On the right side of Figure 15 the arrangements of two or more targets on one rig are shown which support the targets. It could be organized vertically or horizontally and such a system allows the successive production of two or more radionuclides. This system is successfully used in Orsay cyclotron laboratory for the production

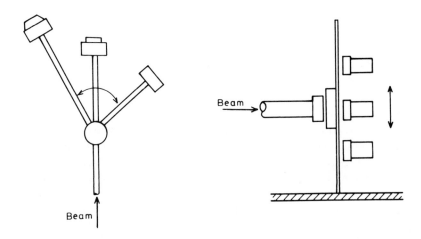

FIGURE 15. Two examples of different arrangement of more targets on the beam stop, to make better use of one beam line.

of short-lived gases. All changes in target positions are remotely controlled. A ring system supporting three target on one beam line have been developed in our laboratory, and can be seen partially in Figure 11b.

H. Manufacture of the Target

As already mentioned, the targets used in accelerator facilities represent a very broad spectrum. This diversity is reflected in the corresponding diversity of the methods used for their manufacture, which embrace virtually all methods known in preparative technology. This work requires special equipment, a well-equipped workshop, and adequate experience.

Sheets and foils are made by a special supplier, cold or hot rolling from pure starting materials. The fabrication of metal foil windows requires the use of electrowelding and vacuum brazing techniques. Thin films on appropriate supports are produced by various techniques including deposition by evaporation in vacuum, cathodic pulverization, electrosputtering, electroplating, electrolysis, and sedimentation. The separation techniques for making ultrathin foils, of the order of 10 μg/cm^2, requires special routines. Special techniques and the recovery of the target material in the preparation of enriched targets have to be used.

The preparation of ''gas in metal'' targets for neutron production requires special impregnation methods. This work needs the availability of hot cells or closed glove boxes. The relatively ready absorption of hydrogen by some metals has led to the use of this property as a means of target preparation for the hydrogen, deuterium, and tritium. Zirconium is a useful metal for this purpose and atomic ratios of hydrogen isotope to metal of about two have been obtained by this method.

The quality control of target materials and mechanical qualities of targets can call virtually all modern testing methods. The most important methods used are chemical analysis, X-ray analysis, spectrography, photometry, metalography, mass spectrography, and activation analysis by neutrons or accelerated particles.

Closely linked with the manufacture of the targets themselves is the construction of special devices for holding and moving the targets. These devices must be adapted to the particular type as well as to the particular function of each target. For these reasons these devices consist mainly of stationary or mobile mountings, holders, sample changers, and various rotating arrangements. Only rarely can target material be used directly as a target. The fundamental support is usually made from the metals with a good thermal conductivity (Al,

Cu, etc.). Irradiated material is attached in appropriate form (foil, layer, pill) on the holder-support. The following methods of preparing targets for irradiation may be used:

1.   Direct cooling of the back side of irradiated foil attached between two O-ring systems.
2.   Attachment of the foil or target plate to the Cu or Al support by clips or screws. A disadvantage is a poor heat transfer from foil to the supported material.
3.   Electrolytic, electroplating, or electrosputtering deposition of the target material on the support. Represents one of the most suitable ways of preparation of the target.
4.   Soldering or melting of the target to the support. Soldering with different solders gives quite good thermal properties, better cooling conditions, but could cause some complications during the chemical separation as other elements are introduced into the system.
5.   Powdered material may be pressed into cavity and covered with a foil against the vacuum in the beam line. Lower beam currents and nondecomposing material which is thermally stable must be used.
6.   Evaporation of the target material in vacuum on some other metal support. Very thin foils may be made, although it is difficult to reach homogen thickness over all irradiated surface.

I. Requirements Imposed on the Targets

Depending on the cyclotron experiments or on the production methods for which the target is intended, the requirements imposed on targets can be very diverse and highly specific and can relate to virtually all physical and chemical properties as well as to the geometric shape and dimensions. In many cases the quality of target could decisively affect the experiment or radionuclide production. The practical applicability of some particular experimental or other method or process may also depend on the suitability of available targets. Frequently required target properties are purity, homogeneity, resistance against pressure, mechanical resistance, thermal and radiation stability.

The following conditions for construction of targets for radionuclide production should satisfy the following requirements:

1.   Choose the nuclear reaction which gives the highest yield at lowest contamination, and use the target material with the lowest price, if possible.
2.   Use the beams of high intensity with a defocused beam spot to avoid destructive heating of the target material. The shortest irradiation time as possible should be received.
3.   Simplest target-target holder construction should be chosen. It is advisable to construct changeable standard components for target hardware which are usable on all beam lines. Maintenance of a long time irradiated defected target can be very complicated. For a routine production there should be a duplicate system in the reserve. It is important to make the working time of the machine effective, while the cost of the beam-on-target time is too high.
4.   Removal of the irradiated target holder from the beam line should be accomplished rapidly and easily and should require as little handling by personnel as possible. If short-lived radionuclides are produced, handling of the target and chemical processing must be undertaken as soon after bombardment as possible. The best way is the use of the on-line separation or fast synthetic techniques. It follows, that the target construction should be as simple as possible and the target holder be free of the contamination, if possible.
5.   Cooling of targets and all parts which are in direct contact with the beam (as, for example, the collimator, foils, and target material) is very important. The best cooling

medium should be chosen (water, silicon oils, and pre-cooled methanol) for each special problem to be solved. The flow and temperature of cooling medium should be remotely controlled during the irradiation and in case of defective function the beam automatically should be shut down. Overheating of the target causes many problems — burn of the foils, loss of very expensive target material, and water in a vacuum chamber, all of which costs time and money.

6.   All components of the target holder could become radioactive to a greater or lesser extent, therefore the selection of material for a target holder should be of great importance.

IV. NUCLEAR DATA; SIMPLE CALCULUS WITH PRACTICAL EXAMPLES AND OPTIMUM IRRADIATION CONDITIONS

The supreme goal of radionuclide production techniques is to attain maximum yield of the desired isotope in a chemical form well suited for fast processing and labeling accompanied by a minimum of unfavorable contaminants.

The yield in radionuclide activity can be roughly estimated before preparation and irradiation by using known physical data of the target-projectile system. The dependence on parameters relevant to the activation procedure, on the other hand, has to be verified by a series of experiments.

In the case of charged particle-induced reactions — in general more laborious than neutron activation — the fundamental considerations are concerned with:

- The choice of the adequate type of nuclear reaction mainly determined by
- The reaction cross-sections for the particles and energies available
- The Q-value or threshold energy, and the Coulombic repulsion barrier, i.e., the starting point of the reaction
- The stopping power defining energy loss and range of the particles in the target and the covering foil(s)
- The optimum energy range dissipated in the target with respect to undesired concurring reactions, and, in special cases
- Scattering effects resulting in beam broadening which could determine the physical dimensions of a thick target

Finally, this ends up in a compromise between as great a target thickness as possible for maximum yield of the desired isotope and minimum yield of the possible contaminants. The "thick target yield" is thus obtained as a sum of more or less "thin target yields".

These latter features are extensively dealt with in Chapter 2. Thus, in the following, we shall restrict our discussion on the physical data mentioned before and their significance for the calculation preparation of the experiments.

A. Cross-Section

The reaction probability is expressed in terms of an effective area or cross-section σ for the target nucleus seen by an impinging particle. Although this quantity is not identical with the physical cross-sectional area, it is frequently of the same order of magnitude and commonly expressed in fractions or barns or millibarns:

$$1 \text{ barn} = 10^{-24} \text{ cm}^2 = 10^3 \text{ millibarns (mb)}$$

Every nucleus exhibits a special cross-section for each of the possible nuclear reactions which, in addition, can vary strongly depending on the kinetic energy E of the particle relative to the target nucleus: $\sigma(E)$ is called excitation function (or yield function). It can have isolated maxima, so-called resonances.

The order of magnitude of nuclear reaction cross-sections ranges from 10^{-32} to $10^{-20} cm^2$. They are usually much smaller than those for atomic collisions being of the order of πa_o^2 (with $a_o = 0.53 \times 10^{-8}$ cm = Bohr radius of the ground state hydrogen atom). They range from 10^{-18} to $10^{-14} cm^2$. Absorption phenomena of charged particles in matter (range, stopping power) are therefore determined by the latter quantity.

σ helps to calculate the number N of nuclear reactions per second per cm^3 of target material of thickness $\Delta x(cm)$ by the equation

$$N = I_p \cdot {}^1N \cdot \sigma \cdot \Delta x \tag{1}$$

with $I_p(sec^{-1})$ = particle current of the particles. ${}^1N$ (cm^{-3}) = number of target nuclei per unit volume (1 cm^3. $I_p = (1/Z) \cdot I$ for a current I (usually measured in μA) for ions of charge Z.

$\Delta\chi$ is assumed so small that neither beam energy nor current are appreciably degraded. Equation 1 can serve as a definition of σ. The total interaction cross-section σ_t is composed of several partial cross-sections for all possible processes like capture (i.e., absorption) σ_a, activation σ_{atc}, scattering σ_s (elastic and inelastic), and fission σ_f, depending on the energy of the particle:

$$\sigma_t = \sigma_a + \sigma_{act} + \sigma_s + \sigma_f$$

Every stable isotope has its own characteristic absorption spectrum. In our context, σ_s is of minor interest as it does not result in a radioactive isotope.

One gets ${}^1N$ in an easy way from

$${}^1N = (\rho/M) N_L$$

with $\rho(g\ cm^{-3})$ = density of the target material; $M(g)$ = its molecular weight (mass number in grams); and N_L = Avogadro's number (6,023 $\times$ 10^{23} atoms per mole).

To relate to the numbers per gram simply divide Equation 1 by ρ:

$$n = I_p n_T \sigma \cdot \Delta x \text{ with } n_T = {}^1N/\rho = N_{L/M} = \text{number of target atoms per gram}$$

Usually, target masses are measured in grams and target thicknesses in grams per cm^2 to get rid of ρ.

Time dependence:

Radioactive nuclei decay with a half-life $T_{1/2}$:

$$- dn = n \lambda dt$$

The decay constant $\lambda = \ln2/T_{1/2}$ follows from the definition

$$n(T_{1/2}) = 1/2\ n(o)$$

Thus, the buildup of transformed nuclei is also a function of time:

$$n(t_1) = I_p n_T \sigma \Delta x \int_{t=o}^{t_1} e^{-\frac{\ln2}{T_{1/2}}(t_1 - t)} dt = I_p n_T \sigma \Delta x\ [1 - \exp(-\lambda t_1)]/\lambda$$

after a period t_1 of activation. If this number is measured at a time t_2 after the reaction was stopped, it will have reduced to

$$n(t_1, t_2) = \frac{1}{\lambda} \, I_p n_T \sigma \Delta x \, [1 - \exp(-\lambda t_1)] \cdot \exp(-\lambda t_2) \qquad (2)$$

$t_2 = 0$ means "end of bombardment" (EOB).

If the target material contains more than one isotope or molecules with the target nucleus as a constituent, the number of activated atoms per gram is given by

$$n = I_p \cdot \frac{N_L}{M} \, \Delta x \sum_i f_i \sigma_i$$

with f_i = relative abundance of isotope i ($f_i \leq 1$) and σ = cross-section for the special nuclear reaction i.

Usually, $M_i = M$ can be taken in front of the summation symbol for an element of several stable nuclides M_i.

The activity of an irradiated sample, i.e., the rate of disintegrations per unit time (= per sec) at time t_2 results in

$$-\frac{dn}{dt_2} = I_p \frac{N_L}{M} \, \sigma \Delta x \, [1 - \exp(-\lambda t_1)] \exp(-\lambda t_2) \qquad (3)$$

This is called the "activation formula".[97]

Its limit for $t_1 \gg T_{1/2}$ at $t_2 = 0$, i.e., its maximum possible value

$$-\frac{dn}{dt} \, (t_1 \to \infty, t_2 = 0) = I_p \frac{N_L}{M} \, \sigma \Delta x$$

is called "saturation activity" (the negative sign on the left side provides for a positive decay rate).

Dimensions:

Activities are measured in: disintegrations per sec = Becquerel (Bq) = sec^{-1} or in Curies: 1 Ci = $3,7 \times 10^{10}$Bq. So, a(Bq) = $3,7 \cdot 10^{10} \cdot$a(Ci). Activities administered in nuclear medical diagnostic procedures range from several hundreds of μCi (about 10×10^6Bq = 10 MBq) to about (10^8Bq = 0.1 GBq).

B. Q-Value, Coulombic Repulsion Barrier, and Threshold Energy

A nuclear reaction can only start at the so-called starting energy E_s where the mass deficit Q — if there is any — of the reacting partners as well as the electrostatic repulsion potential E_c (only relevant for charged particle induced processes) is at least balanced by the kinetic energy $E_1 + E_2$ of the initial system m_1, m_2 (see Figure 17).

In laboratory coordinates, m_2 is at rest in general: $E_2 = 0$. So, the impinging particle 1 has to provide for the starting energy E_s which is a function of Q and E_c:

$$E_1 \geq E_s = f(Q, E_c)$$

By definition, the mass difference between the initial and final states is

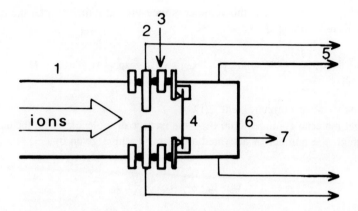

FIGURE 16.   Basic set-up of a radionuclide target system for charged particle interactions.

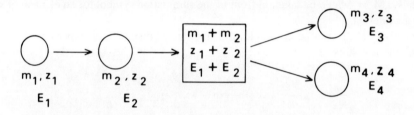

FIGURE 17.   Principle of two body nuclear reaction.

$$Q = [(m_1 + m_2) - (m_3 + m_4)] \cdot c^2/MeV$$

A nuclear mass m can be put together from the masses of its nucleus (with number A) and the "mass excess", accounting for the binding energy and the differences of the neutron and proton masses from the mass unit u:

$$m = A \cdot u + \Delta, \text{ or:}$$

$$\Delta = m - A \cdot \Delta\bar{u}$$

with m(g) = mass of the neutral atom which is, to some 10^{-3}, equal to the nuclear mass (neglecting the atomic electrons and their binding energies); A = nucleon number (mass number); u = atomic mass unit, for example ^{12}C.

$$\text{nuclear mass} = \frac{1}{12} \times \frac{m(^{12}C)}{\text{Avogadro's number}} = \frac{1}{12} \times \frac{12g}{6,023 \times 10^{23}} = 1,66 \times 10^{-24} \text{ g}$$

or, in the energy scale:

$$1\mu = 931.14 \text{ MeV} \rightarrow \text{mass unit}$$

As a coarse rule:

$$1 \text{ milli-mass unit } (1\text{mu}) \approx 1 \text{ MeV}$$

To calculate Q, we thus are able to use the equivalent equation

$$Q = [(\Delta_1 + \Delta_2) - (\Delta_2 + \Delta_3)] \times c^2/\text{MeV} \qquad (4)$$

which is more convenient, since rather the Δ's than the m's are found in atomic mass tables.[99]

Q is somehow analogous to the "heat effect" in chemical processes. It can either be negative (Q < o: endoergic reaction) or positive (Q > o: exoergic). In the latter case, if additionally E_c is small (for low Z target nuclei):

$$E_{thr} = 0, \text{ and } E_s \approx 0$$

so the reaction starts actually at zero or very low energy of the accelerated particle.

The special case $m_1 = m_3$ is called scattering:

$$Q = 0: \text{ elastic}$$

$$Q < 0: \text{ inelastic}$$

Example: consider the reactions (a) $^{10}B(d,n)$ and (b) $^{11}B(d,2n)$ both leading to the short-lived radionuclide $^{11}C(T_{1/2} = 20,3 \text{ min})$:
here:

$$\Delta_1 = \Delta(^{10}B) \text{ or } \Delta(^{11}B), \text{ respectively}$$

$$\Delta_2 = \Delta(d)$$

$$\Delta_3 = \Delta(n) \text{ or} \Delta(2n), \text{ respectively}$$

$$\Delta_4 = \Delta(^{11}C)$$

Numerical values: Hence we get:

$\Delta(^{10}B) = + 12,939 \times 10^{-3}u$ (a) $Q = (27,041 - 20,095) \times 10^{-3} u$
$\Delta(^{11}B) = + 9,305 \times 10^{-3}u$ $= + 6,946 \text{ mu} = + 6,5 \text{ MeV}$
$\Delta(d) = + 14,102 \times 10^{-3}u$
$\Delta(n) = + 8,665 \times 10^{-3}u$ (b) $Q = (23,407 - 28,76) \times 10^{-3}u$
$\Delta(^{11}C) = + 11,430 \times 10^{-3}u$ $= - 5,353 \text{ mu} = - 5 \text{ MeV}$

Consequently, reaction (a) can start provided the Coulombic repulsion has been compensated, (b) cannot.

Coulombic barrier:

Two bodies carrying charges $z_1 \cdot e$ and $z_2 \cdot e$ (e = elementary charge), at a distance r, experience a mutual force

$$K = \frac{z_1 z_2 e^2}{r^2}$$

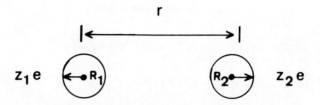

FIGURE 18.   Coulomb interaction.

or a potential

$$U = \frac{z_1 z_2 e^2}{r}$$

Two positively charged particles approaching one another to a minimum possible distance r_{min} have to overcome the repulsive Coulomb potential

$$E_c = \frac{z_1 z_2 e^2}{r_{min}}$$

with $r_{min} = R_1 + R_2$, before the highly attractive nuclear forces begin to become effective.

From $R_i = R_o \times A_i^{1/3}$ with $R_o = 1{,}2 \times 10^{-13}$ cm ($\pm$ 10%) for the "electromagnetic radius" of the nucleus[98] and A_i = atomic number (i = 1,2) it follows that

$$r_{min} = R_o \times (A_1^{1/3} + A_2^{1/3})$$

Hence

$$E_c = \frac{z_1 z_2 e^2}{R_o(A_1^{1/3} + A_2^{1/3})}$$

On the basis of the simplifying approximations

$$z_1 \ll z_2 (\text{i.e., } A_1 \ll A_2), z_2 \approx \frac{A_2}{2}$$

we get the rough estimate

$$E_c = \frac{z_1 z_2^{2/3} \cdot e^2}{2^{1/3} \cdot R_o} = 0.95 \cdot z_1 z_2^{2/3} \text{ (MeV) after inserting}$$

$$e^2 = \alpha \hbar c = 1.44 \times 10^{-7} \text{ eV cm}$$

There is, however, a certain probability increasing with energy that the incoming charged particles are able to penetrate the Coulombic barrier E_c even if $E_1 < E_c$ ("tunneling effect").

So, E_c itself is not very relevant for reaction kinetics, since only a certain fraction E_{cc}^{eff} which has to be determined by experiment establishes a real "well".

For light elements ($z_2 \leqslant 10$) bombarded with p or d ($z_1 = 1$) or He-ions ($z_1 = 2$), this effective Coulomb barrier E_{cc}^{eff} is smaller than 2 MeV or $\leqslant$ 3 MeV, respectively, and thus hardly affects the starting energy of reactions with light nuclei at energies provided by even the smallest cyclotrons in use.

Example:

$$^{10}B \, (d,n)^{11}C, \, z_1 = 1, \, z_2 = 5 \, (= 1/2 \, A_2), \, E_c \cong 0.95 \cdot 1 \cdot 5^{2/3} \text{ MeV} = 2,9 \text{ MeV}$$

In fact, the reaction starts at about 0,25 MeV.[101]

Threshold energy:

As mentioned at the beginning of this section, $Q < 0$ has to be provided for by the kinetic energy of the initial system. Usually, the target nucleus m_2 is at rest: $E_2 = 0$. From the kinetic energy E_1 of the bombarding particle in laboratory coordinates the fraction

$$1/2 \, (m_1 + m_2) \cdot v_{CM}^2 = 1/2 \, (m_1 + m_2) \cdot \left(\frac{m_1}{m_1 + m_2} \right)^2 \cdot v_1^2 = \frac{m_1}{m_1 + m_2} \cdot E_1$$

is transferred to the motion of the center-of-mass (CM). It follows that only the fraction

$$E = E_1 \left(1 - \frac{m_1}{m_1 + m_2} \right) = E_1 \cdot \frac{m_2}{m_1 + m_2} \text{ is available for compensating}$$

is available for compensating $Q < 0$. Thus, we get the condition

$$E_1 \cdot \frac{m_2}{m_1 + m_2} \geqslant |Q| \text{ (which is a positive quantity)}$$

or

$$E_{thr} = -Q \cdot \frac{m_1 + m_2}{m_2} = -Q \cdot \left(1 + \frac{m_1}{m_2} \right)$$

$$= -Q \left(1 + \frac{A_1}{A_2} \right)$$

$$E_{thr} = 0 \text{ if } Q \geqslant 0 \tag{5}$$

A reaction with $Q < 0$ consequently starts if the bombarding particle has at least a "starting energy" E_s in the laboratory system of $-Q(1 + A_1/A_2)$ or E_c^{eff}, whichever is greater.

Examples:

(a) $^{10}B \, (d,n), Q = +6.5 \text{ MeV}, E_c^{eff} \approx 0 \Rightarrow E_s \cong 0$

(b) $^{11}B \, (d,2n), Q = -5 \text{ MeV}, E_c^{eff} \approx 0$

$$E_s = E_{thr} = +5 \text{ MeV} \times (1 + 2/11) = 5.9 \text{ MeV}$$

Experimental values:

(a) $E_s = E_{thr} \cong 0.5 \text{ MeV}^{(102)}$

(b) $E_{thr} = 5.89 \text{ MeV}^{(59)}$

C. Energy Loss, Stopping Power, and Range

Swift charged particles ($m_1 \gg m_0$ = electron mass, and charge $z_1 e$) penetrating through an absorber of thickness Δx (cm) will lose their kinetic energy E (MeV) predominantly by inelastic collisions with the atomic electrons of the stopping material, i.e., by excitation and ionization. This is valid for intermediate energies (for protons: $0,5 \text{ MeV} \leqslant E \leqslant 1000 \text{ MeV}$).

The infrequent, though important nuclear reactions can be neglected here. Detailed information is given in Chapter 2 and References 98 and 99.

The tabulated data, from which

stopping power $S = -\dfrac{1}{\rho} \dfrac{dE}{dX'}$

energy loss $\dfrac{dE}{dX'}$ and

range R   (cm or mg cm^{-2})

can be directly taken or easily derived for every target or foil material of density ρ, are based on the "Bethe formula"[103] for the specific energy loss

$$\frac{dE}{dx} = \frac{4\pi z_1^2 e^4}{m_0 c^2 \beta^2} NZ_2 \left[\ln \frac{2m_0 c^2 \beta^2}{Ia(1 - \beta^2)} - \beta^2 - \frac{C}{Z_2} \right] = \frac{4\pi z_1^2 e^4}{m_0 c^2 \beta^2} NB \qquad (6)$$

with the following definitions: c = speed of light (3×10^{10}cm/sec); $\beta = v/c$ = velocity of the incident particle in units of c; N = number of atoms per unit target volume ($N \cdot Z_2$ = number of electrons per unit target volume); I_a = geometric mean of the excitation and ionization potentials of the absorbing atoms I_a = const. $\cdot z_2$ for higher z_2 i.e., for a Thomas-Fermi electron charge distribution ($I_9 \approx 164 \text{ eV}$ for aluminum). C = correction due to the binding of the inner shell electrons. C is of the order of 1, so

$$C/z_2 \ll \ln \frac{2m_0 V^2}{I_a}$$

turns out to be a small correction of the "atomic stopping number" B, at least in our context.* The above formula holds for reactions with

$$\frac{z_2}{137} \ll \frac{v}{c} \ll \frac{137}{2z_1 z_2}$$

---

*   c/z accounts for nonparticipating electrons at the energy loss.

i.e., in most practical cases of light ions bombarding targets of not too high z_2.
Evaluation is greatly facilitated by the following few relations:

$$\beta^2 = \frac{v_1^2}{c^2} = \frac{1}{2} \, m_1 v_1^2 / \frac{1}{2} \, m_1 c^2 = \frac{E_1}{1/2 \, A_1 uc^2}$$

$$= \frac{2}{A_1} \cdot \frac{E_1 \, (MeV)}{931 \, MeV}$$

$$m_0 c^2 = 0.511 \, MeV$$

$$e^2 = \alpha hc = 1.44 \cdot 10^{-7} \, eV \, cm$$

Range:

From the definition of stopping power S we may deduce

$$dx = -dE/pS \text{ or}$$

$$R = \frac{1}{p} \int_0^{E_0} dE/S = -\int_0^{E_0} \frac{dE}{(dE/pdx)}$$

for a particle coming to rest (E = 0). If the initial energy E_0 should only decrease to a
certain value $E_1 < E_0$ (e.g., to suppress a competitive process in the range $E_1 < E < E_0$),
the ion beam has to pass a slab of thickness

$$x_1 = \frac{1}{p} \int_{E_1}^{E_0} \frac{dE}{S}$$

Conversely, the energy loss after penetration of a material layer Δx is given by integrating

$$dE = -pSdx \text{ over } 0 \leqslant x \leqslant \Delta x:$$

$$\Delta E = -p \int_0^{\Delta x} Sdx = \int_0^{\Delta x} \left(\frac{dE}{dx}\right) dx \text{ and } E_1 = E_0 - \Delta E$$

In the case Δx is so large that dE/dx or S varies appreciably between entering and leaving
the absorbing layer it has to be put together by several slabs thin enough to calculate

$$\Delta E_i = -\int_{X_i}^{X_{i+1}} S(E_i) \, dx = -S(E_i) (X_{i+1} - X_i) \text{ with } S(E_i) = \text{const., and } E_1 = E_0 - \sum_i \Delta E_i$$

Since S rather depends on $v = \sqrt{2E/m}$ than on E, range and stopping powers are tabulated
or drawn as functions of E/ m.[100]

Examples:

(a)   Energy loss of 16 MeV deuterons in a 50 μ-Al-foil (ρ_{Al} = 2.7 gcm^{-3}): 50 μ Al =
        50 × 10^{-4}cm × 2.7 gcm^{-3} = 13.5 mgcm^{-2} (E/m)$_d$ = 1/2(E/m)$_p$ = 1/2 × 16 MeV/
        amu = 8 MeV/amu. From the table we read S = 0,040 MeV/mgcm^{-2} for hydrogen

ions on aluminum (it is also valid for deuterons if we choose the right E/m). So, $\Delta E = - S(\rho \Delta x) = - 0.04$ MeV/mgcm^{-2} $\times$ 13.5 mgcm^{-2} $= - 0.54$ Mev.

Consequently, the energy of the deuterium beam is degraded by the foil to about 15.5 MeV available for nuclear reactions, e.g., B(d.xn).

(b)   The range of 16 MeV-d in Al would be (see table "range" for E/m = 8 MeV/amu): 116.062 mgcm^{-2} which, by dividing by ρ = 2.7 $\times$ 10^3 mgcm^{-3}, gives Δx = 43 $\times$ 10^{-3} cm = 0.43 mm.

Range and stopping power in compounds:

For a target material of molecular weight M composed of atoms with atomic weights M_i and fractions f_i:

$$M = \frac{\Sigma f_i M_i}{\Sigma f_i}$$

This "additivity rule" helps to find the stopping power relative to a reference material (subscript 0, usually aluminum):

$$\frac{(dE/\rho dx) \text{ compound}}{(dE/\rho dx)_0} = \frac{1}{M} \Sigma \frac{f_i M_i \, (dE/\rho dx)_i}{(dE/\rho dx)_0}$$

Graphs of the ratios of $(dE/\rho dx)_i$: $(dE/\rho dx)_0$ as a function of E/m are also shown in Reference 100.

Similar considerations apply to the range R. Calculation, e.g., by numerical integration, is tendious. A rough estimate of the range in a compound is given by the Bragg-Kleeman rule[98]

$$R \cdot \rho/\sqrt{M} = \text{const.}$$

The accuracy is about $\pm$ 15%. Here the "effective molecular weight" $\sqrt{M}$ is defined by:

$$\sqrt{M} = \Sigma f_i M_i / \Sigma f_i \sqrt{M_i}$$

Example: range of 15.5 MeV deuterons in boron-trioxide $B_2O_3 (\rho = 1.84$ gcm^{-3}): $f_1 = 2$, $M_1 = 10,81$, $f_2 = 3$, $M_2 = 16$, $\sqrt{M} = 69,62/18,58 = 3,75$.

Reference material: Al (ρ = 2.7 gcm^{-3}) with $\sqrt{M} = \sqrt{27} = 5.2$. R(E/m = 8 MeV) = 116.06 mgcm^{-2}. As a constant in the Bragg-Kleeman rule we take (R $\times$ ρ/M)$_{Al}$. So, with these data

$$R(B_2O_3) = \left(\frac{\sqrt{M}}{\rho}\right) B_2O_3 \times \left(\frac{R \cdot \rho}{\sqrt{M}}\right) Al$$

$$= \frac{3.75}{1.84 \text{ gcm}^{-3}} \times \frac{116.06 \text{ mgcm}^{-2} \times 2.7 \text{ gcm}^{-3}}{5.2}$$

$$= 122.8 \text{ mgcm}^{-2} \text{ or, with } \rho = 1.84 \text{ gcm}^{-3}$$

$$= 66.7 \times 10^{-3} \text{cm} \approx 0.7 \text{ mm } (\pm 15\%)$$

The ranges and energies are calculated with the assumption, that particles always penetrate in a forward direction. Due to multiple scattering the real range is not only shorter than the calculated one, it is also uncertain to some extent. So is the energy.

The widths of the distribution functions (which is a measure of this uncertainty) are called range or energy straggling, respectively.

These effects, however, are of minor concern in our context: The thick target yield is not affected by the energy straggling at energies above, say, 100 keV.[104] On the other hand, the physical target cross-section should allow for the beam broadening, near the end of the range, if necessary.

D. Yield

Let us start from the activation formula (III) for one particular reaction with cross-section $\sigma(cm^2)$ between a beam I_p or particles of charge z·e with nuclei of mass number M:

$$-\frac{dn}{dt} = I_p \cdot \frac{L}{M} \, \sigma \Delta x \, [1 - \exp(-\lambda t)]$$

with $I_p = 1/z$, I = ion beam current (elementary charges per sec):

$$\Delta x = \frac{\Delta E}{(dE/dx)} \quad \text{with dx standing for } \rho \cdot dx \text{ (mgcm}^{-2}\text{) as usual}$$

$$N_L = \text{Avogardo's number} = 6.023 \times 10^{23} \text{ particles/mole,}$$

$$\lambda = \frac{\ln 2}{T1/2}$$

The decay factor $\exp(-\lambda t_2)$ has been omitted because it is meaningless before EOB.

The expression holds for a thin layer Δx as explained earlier. To get maximum possible activity of the product nuclide, one has to integrate over the whole range $O \leqslant x \leqslant R$ or, on the energy scale, $E_s \leqslant E \leqslant E_0$:

$$-\frac{dn}{dt} = I_p \frac{L}{M} \, [1 - \exp(-\lambda t)] \int_{E_s}^{E_0} \frac{\sigma(E)}{(dE/dx)} \, dE$$

One could substitute E_s by zero, as the integral vanishes for $E \leqslant E_s$. The limit $- dn/dt$ $(t \to \infty)$, i.e. for $t \gg T_{1/2}$, is again called saturation activity

$$A_s = I_p \frac{L}{M} \int_0^{E_0} \frac{\sigma(E)}{(dE/dx)} \, dE \qquad (7)$$

This is the maximum activity which can be produced by a particle current $I_p(sec^{-1})$ of energy E(MeV) in a thick target.

Measured in μCi, and related to an ion beam current of 1 μA, the quantity

$$A_s/I = Y$$

is called "Thick Target Yield". Obviously, "thick target" means a slab of material thick enough to degrade the energy to at least E_s.

With the conversion factors:

for A_s: 1 μCi = $3.7 \times 10^4 \text{sec}^{-1}$
for I_p: 1 elementary charge/sec = 1.602×10^{-13}μA
for σ: 1 millibarn (1 mb) = 10^{-27}cm^2

we recalculate

$$Y = \frac{1}{ZM} \cdot \frac{6.023 \cdot 10^{23}}{3.7\ 10^4} \cdot \frac{10^{-27}}{1.602 \cdot 10^{-13}} \int_0^{E_0} \frac{\sigma(E)}{(dE/dx)}\ dE$$

$$= 1.016 \cdot 10^5 \frac{1}{Z \cdot M} \int_0^{E_0} \frac{\sigma(E)}{(dE/dx)}\ dE \left(\frac{\mu Ci}{\mu A}\right) \qquad (8)$$

if σ(E) is given in millibarns.

In case the bombarded layer is thin, i.e., the ions emerge with a kinetic energy $E_1 > E_s$ the yield from this target is clearly given by

$$Y' = Y(E_0) - Y(E_1)$$

If the target material consists of different stable nuclides or molecules, the yield has to be corrected for the relative abundance of the special target nucleus. Yield curves and corrections are given in Reference 105.

Example: ^{123}I-production with a 30 MeV-p-compact cyclotron via ^{124}Te(p,2n)^{123}I.

From the excitation functions for the reactions ^{124}Te(p,2n)^{123}I and ^{124}Te(p,n)^{124}I[52] we can conclude, that ^{124}I-contamination will be smallest if we choose the energy range from 28 MeV to 18 MeV. Usually, enriched ^{124}Te is taken in the chemical form of TeO_2. We restrict our yield estimate to the case of (nearly) 100% enriched ^{124}Te to avoid contamination by ^{125}Te(p,2n)^{124}I, ^{125}Te(p,n)^{125}I, etc.

E. Foil Thicknesses, Example of ^{123}I Production

From chemical reasons (corrosion by evaporized TeO_2), a Pt-foil (ρ = 21.45 gcm^{-3}) of, say, 50 μ thickness is recommended as a direct cover for the target sample.

For ease of handling, an additional foil of nickel (ρ = 8.9 gcm^{-3} or havar or stainless steel as well, of, say, 0.1 mm thickness would be of advantage to close the beam line vacuum and may be provide a stream of cooled He-gas between the foils in case the proton beam current should be higher than about 10 μA.

By this upstream nickel foil the proton energy will be degraded by

$$\Delta E = \rho \Delta x (dE/dx)_{30MeV} = 8900\ \text{mgcm}^{-3} \times 0.01\ \text{cm} \times 0.012\ \text{MeV/mgcm}^{-2} = 1.07\ \text{MeV}$$

We have derived here $(dE/dx)_{Ni,30MeV} = 0.012$ MeV/gcm^{-2} from $(dE/dx)_{Ni}/(dE/dx)_{Al} = 0.88$ and $(dE/dx)_{Al} = 0.014$ MeV/mgcm^{-2} (extrapolated from Figures 9 and 2 in Reference 4, respectively).

With this, the protons enter the Pt-foil with an energy of about 29 MeV. Here, they loose

$$\Delta E(\text{Pt}) = \rho \cdot \Delta x \cdot (dE/dx)_{\text{Pt}} = 21.45 \times 10^3 \text{ mgcm}^{-3} \times 0.005 \text{ cm} \times 0.0084 \text{ MeV/gcm}^{-2} = 0.9 \text{ MeV}$$

again, we took $(dE/dx)_{\text{Pt}} = (dE/x)_{\text{Au}} = 0.6(dE/dx)_{\text{Al}}$ for 29MeV.

Thus, the proton beam enters the TeO_2-target material with an energy of $30 - 1.07 - 0.9 \cong 28$ MeV, as proposed.

Range in TeO_2: $R(E_1 — E_2) = R(E_1 = 28 \text{ MeV}) - R(E_2 = 18 \text{ MeV})$.

Following the Bragg-Kleeman Rule for a compound we get

$$R(\text{TeO}_2) = (\sqrt{M}/\rho)_{\text{TeO}_2} \times (R\rho/\sqrt{M})_{\text{Al}}$$

with the following data:

	TeO$_2$		Al	
E (MeV)	28	18	28	18
R (mgcm^{-2})	?	?	1020	480
ρ (gcm^{-3})	5.8		2.7	
	8.2		5.2	

with this: $R(\text{TeO}_{2,28\text{MeV}}) = (8.2/5.8) \times (1020 \times 2.7/5.2) = 748$ mgcm and $R(\text{TeO}_{2,18\text{MeV}}) = 352$ mgcm^{-2}, so $R(28 \rightarrow 18 \text{ MeV}) = 748 - 352 = 396$ mgcm$^{-2} = 0.7$ mm.

With a target diameter of, say, 1 cm we need a sample of $(0.5 \text{ cm})^2 \pi \times 0.07 \text{ cm} \times 5.8 \text{ gcm}^{-3} = 0.32 \text{ g} = 320$ mg of enriched $^{124}\text{TeO}_2$. The rest of the proton energy is then dissipated in the water-cooled target backing.

Yield:

Basic data:	^{124}Te(p,2n) ^{123}I $E_s = 11$ MeV		^{124}Te(p,n) ^{124}I $E_s = 6$ MeV	
E_p (MeV)	28	18	28	18
$E_p - E_s$ (MeV)	17	7	22	12
Y (μCi/μA)	7×10^5	7×10^4	1.3×10^5	0.9×10^5
$T_{1/2}$ (hr)	13		101	
λ (hr^{-1})	0.0533		0.00686	

The Y-values are taken from Reference 105.

The Y-values are taken from Reference 105.

As $^{124}\text{TeO}_2$ consists of 80% ^{124}Te by weight, $Y(\text{TeO}_2) = 0.8$ Y(Te), so $Y(^{123}\text{I}, 17 \text{ MeV}) - Y(^{123}\text{I}, 7 \text{ MeV}) = 0.8 \times 6.3 \cdot 10^5 \mu\text{Ci}/\mu\text{A} = 504 \text{ mCi}/\mu\text{A}$. $Y(^{124}\text{I}, 22 \text{ MeV}) - Y(^{124}\text{I}, 12 \text{ MeV}) = 0.8 \times 0.4 \cdot 10^5 \mu\text{Ci}/\mu\text{A} = 32 \text{ mCi}/\mu\text{A}$.

After a bombardment by $I = 1\mu$A for $t = 1$hr (charge 1μAhr) the activity $A = Y \cdot I$ $(1 - \exp(-\lambda t))$ will be $Y(^{123}\text{I}) = 504 \times 0.052 \cong 26 \text{ mCi}/\mu\text{Ahr}$; $Y(^{124}\text{I}) = 32 \times 0.00684 \cong 0.22 \text{ mCi}/\mu\text{Ahr}$.

The iodine-124-contamination will, in this case of very highly enriched ^{124}Te, be $Y(^{124}I)/Y(^{123}I) = 0.85\%$ which would be the unavoidable minimum.

In view of the roughness of the estimate these results compare very well with experiment (see Table 4 of Reference (52):

Using ^{124}Te (enrichment 99.87%), with $E_p = 27$ MeV→12 . . . 13 MeV (target thickness 519 mgcm^{-2}), $Y(^{123}I)$ = 20.4mCi/μAhr with a 0.62% contamination of ^{124}I.

In practical cases, ^{124}TeO$_2$ is taken enriched to 91 . . . 96%. Yields of several hundreds of mCi of ^{123}I are achieved after 2 hr of bombardment with, say, 20 μA of protons. Contamination is about 1% of ^{124}I at EOB. It can be used until this figure has raised to 4%, i.e., for a "shelf-life" of $2 \times T_{1/2}(^{123}I) \cong 1d$.

Even with smaller cyclotrons ($E_p = 20$ MeV) this method of ^{123}I production can be applied. Yield is about 2 to 3 mCi/μAhr with a ^{124}I-contamination of 1% at EOB, then.

V. SOURCES OF NUCLEAR PARTICLES

Practical amounts of radioactivity are produced today by nuclear reactions with only a handful of particles: neutrons (n), protons (p), deuterons (d), and helium ions (^{3}He^{++}, ^{4}He^{++} = α). The bulk of the work actually is accomplished by irradiation with n and p, at a few older cyclotrons preferably with d and α. Neutron-induced reactions, i.e,

- Neutron capture or radiative capture (n,γ) with slow neutrons
- Spallation (n,x$_1$n x$_2$p x$_3$α . . .), x$_i$ = 0,1,2,. . .), with fast neutrons
- Fission (n,f)

all occur in fission neutron reactions, the techniques of production, however, being quite different from those using energetic ions.

Fast neutron generators or cyclotron neutron sources, because of their low neutron flux density, are used nowadays mainly for analytical purposes via neutron activation analysis or for high-LET radiation therapy. We shall discuss these types of neutron facilities only briefly.

The most versatile source of charged particles of adequate beam currents is the cyclotron. Recently, one high-current 30 MeV-p, resonant linear accelerator (LINAC) is being installed for isotope production, exclusively.

Small electrostatic ion accelerators (Van-de-Graaffs and Cockcroft-Walton generators) have been used for experimental work with low activities in former times. All big LINACs (Tandem-Van-de-Graaffs, resonant LINACs) are mainly devoted to basic physics research. In the fields of biosciences, they are partly employed for analytical procedures like charged particle activation analysis or back scatter ionometry and, as X-ray or fast neutron sources, for structural analysis in biochemistry. Their operation is too costly for routine work like "isotope factories".

Electrons, on the other hand, are confined to electromagnetic interactions with too low cross-sections as needed for large-scale radionuclide production.

Investigation of the excitation functions of most relevant charged particle nuclear reactions leads to the conclusion that energies up to, say, 35 or 40 MeV (for protons, other particles corresponding to their charges and masses) are sufficient for producing nearly all radionuclides needed in biomedical applications. There are only a few exceptions, e.g., ^{127}I(p,5n) ^{123}Xe, which decays to the widely used ^{123}I. This one, however, can well be derived from ^{124}Te(p,2n)^{123}I with a maximum cross-section of more than 1000 mb at about 27 MeV. Thus,

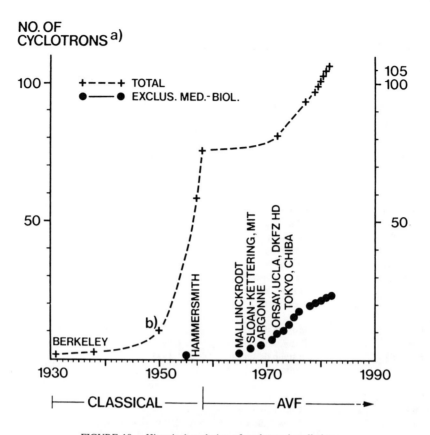

FIGURE 19.   Historical evolution of cyclotron installations.

we shall restrict our discussion to (1) small cyclotrons — compact or medical, (2) the resonant LINAC, (3) the nuclear fission reactor, supplemented by a glance on, (4) fast neutron generators and other neutrons sources.

A. Cyclotrons

Lawrence and Livingston[106] built the first cyclotron in 1932, which accelerated protons to an energy of 1.2 MeV only a few months after the linear accelerator of Sloan and Lawrence had supplied mercury ions of 1.26 MeV.[9]

Since the early 1930s, the cyclotron has developed to be the most powerful tool in radionuclide production. With good reasons, (small) cyclotrons are called the "workhorses" among charged particle accelerators: they yield adequate beam currents and operation is not as costly as that of linear accelerators with comparable output. From the beginning, cyclotrons have been destined rather for applications in life sciences and radiochemistry than in physics.

The principle of focusing particles by an azimuthally varying magnetic field (AVF) was the basis of the construction of smaller and more efficient compact cyclotrons in the years after 1956. Presently, there are approximately 90 cyclotrons in operation all over the world (see Figure 19).

A recent compilation of most existing cyclotrons is given by Martin.[107] Cyclotrons with the facilities for radionuclide production, mostly for medical use, are listed in Table 7.

The acceleration of ions (produced in the electric discharge of an ion source) in a cyclotron is accomplished in many equally spaced steps corresponding to energy gains of 30 to 40 keV. The beam is repeatedly passed through the slits of (one to three) specially formed electrodes, the "dees", carrying an alternating voltage in resonance with the system. Fre-

Table 7
CYCLOTRONS WITH FACILITIES FOR RADIONUCLIDE PRODUCTION[a]

Location	Institution	e/m of accelerated particles[b]	Maximum energy (for p)/MeV	Manufacturer[c]
Australia:				
Sydney or elbourne[d]		1	42	TCC
Austria:		1	42	TCC
Vienna[e]	University			
Belgium:				
Louvain-la-Neuve (CYCLONE)	Université Catholique de Louvain	1 1/2	95	CGR
Liège	University	1 1/2 2/3	22	CGR
Brussels[e]	University	1 1/2 2/3	40	CGR
Leuven[d]	AZ St. Raphael	1 ?		
Fleurus[e]	*Institutdes Radio-éléments	1	90	CGR
Brazil:				
Rio de Janeiro	Instituto de Engenharia Nuclear	1 1/2	24	TCC
Sao Paulo	Instituto de Energia Atômica	1 1/2 2/3	24	TCC
Canada:				
Vancouver, B.C.	*TRIUMF	1	520	
	University of B.C.	1	42	TCC[c]
Edmonton, Alberta[d]	*Cross Cancer Institute (MARIA)	1, heavy ions		
China:				
Shanghai[f]	Inst. f. Nucl. Res.	1 1/2	30	
Cuba:				
Havanna[d]	Inst. de Oncologia y Radiobiologia			
Finland:				
Åbo	Åbo Academi	1 1/2 2/3	19	USSR
Yväskylä	University	1 1/2 2/3	20	Scanditronix
France:				
Orléan	*Centre National de Recherche Scientifique	1 1/2	36	CGR
Orsay	Hôpital d'Orsay	1 1/2 2/3	24	CGR
Saclay[e]	*Atomic Energy Commission	1 1/2 2/3	40	CCR
Nice (MEDICIYC)	University	1	50	
Lyon	Université Cl. Bernard	1/2	28 (for d)	
Germany Fed. Rep.:				
Essen	Klinikum, Radiol. Center	1 1/2 2/3	24	TCC
Hannover	Med. Hochschule	1 1/2 2/3	35	Scanditronix
Heidelberg	German Cancer Research Center	1 1/2 2/3	21,5	AEG
Jülich	*Kernforschungs-anage			

Table 7 (continued)
CYCLOTRONS WITH FACILITIES FOR RADIONUCLIDE PRODUCTION[a]

Location	Institution	e/m of accelerated particles[b]	Maximum energy (for p)/MeV	Manufacturer[c]
	a) Inst. f. Kern-physik	1 1/2 2/3	45	AEG
	b) Inst. f. Fest-körperforschung	1 1/2 2/3	24	TCC
Karlsruhe	*Inst. f. Angewandte Kernphysik	1/2	26	AEG
		1[5])	42	TCC
Munich[d]	Krankenhaus rechts d. Isar	1 1/2	~50	
Germany Dem. Rep.:				
Rossendorf	Zentralinst. f. Kern-forschung d. Akad. d. Wissenschaften	1/2	21	USSR
Berlin-Buch[d]	Inst. For Applied Isotope Research d. Akad. d. Wiss.	1 1/2	~40	USSR
India:				
Calcutta	Bhaba Atomic Res. Center	1 1/2	60	
Italy:				
Milan	a) University of Milan	1	45	
	b) University of Milan Hospital	1 1/2 2/3	35	Scanditronix[e] CGR
Pisa[d]	University	?		
Japan:				
Chiba	NIRS	1 1/2 2/3	70	CGR
Hyogo	*Medi-Physics	1 1/2 2/3	26	TCC
Sendai	Tohoku University	1 1/2 2/3	40	CGR
Tokyo	IMS	1 1/2 2/3	26	TCC
Netherlands:				
Eindhoven	University of echnology	1 1/2 2/3	30	Philips
Groningen	Kernfysich Versneller Inst.	1/2, heavy ions	140 (for α)	Philips
Petten	*Philips-Duphar	1 1/2 2/3	30	Philips
Norway:				
Oslo	Fysisk Inst. Univ.	1 1/2 2/3	35	Scanditronix
Poland:				
Warshaw	University	No data available		
South Africa:				
Pretoria	Council for Sci. a. Industr. Res.	1 1/2 2/3	15	
Faure CP	Nat. Accel. Ctr.	1 1/2 2/3	8	
Saudi Arabia:				
Riyadh	King Faisal Res. Center	1 1/2 2/3	26	TCC

Table 7 (continued)
CYCLOTRONS WITH FACILITIES FOR RADIONUCLIDE PRODUCTION[a]

Location	Institution	e/m of accelerated particles[b]	Maximum energy (for p)/MeV	Manufacturer[c]
Sweden:				
Stockholm	Res. Inst. of	1 1/2 (and		
	Physics	$^{12}C^{4+}$)	15	
	Karolinska Hosp.	1	16	Scanditronix
Switzerland:				
Villingen	*Swiss Inst. for			
	Nucl. Res. (SIN)			
	Injector I	1	72	Philips
	Injector II	1	72	
Lausanne[d]	Ctr. Hosp. Univ.	?		
	Voudois			
Czechoslowakia:				
Rez	Czechoslowak		U 120	USSR
	Acad. of Sci.			
United Kingdom:				
London	*Med. Res. Council	1/2	16(for d)	
Clatterbridge[e]	Med Res. Council	1	65	Scanditronix
Harwell	*AERE	1, heavy	59	
		ions		
Amersham	*The Radiochem.	a) 1 1/2	27	
	Ctr. Ltd.	b) 1[d]	42	TCC
USA:				
Argonne, Ill.	Argonne Nat. Lab.	1/2 2/3	11	
	Cancer Res. Hosp.	1 1/2 2/3	15	TCC
Arlington	*Medi-Physics	a) 1 1/2 2/3	40	Scanditronix
Heights, Ill.		b) 1 1/2 2/3	40[d]	Scanditronix
Chicago, Ill.	Fr. McLean Memo-	1 1/2 2/3	15	TCC
	rial Res. Inst.			
Emeryville, Ca.	*Medi-Physics	1 1/2 2/3	22	TCC
South Plain-				
field, N.J.	*Medi-Physics	1 1/2 2/3	22	TCC
Miami Beach, Fl.	Mt. Sinai Med. Ctr.	1 1/2 2/3	26.5	TCC
Cleveland, Ohio	*NASA-Lewis-			
	Res. Center	1 1/2 2/3	46	
N. Billerica, Ma.	*New England			
	Nuclear Corp.	1 1/2 2/3	22	TCC
	(NEN)			
		1	26	TCC
New York	Sloan-Kettering-	1 1/2 2/3	15	TCC
	Inst. f. Cancer Res.			
Baltimore, Md.	John Hopkins	1	16	Scanditronix
	Hosp.			
Houston, Texas	M. D. Anderson			
	Hosp. a. Tumor			
	Inst.	1	42	TCC
Davis, Ca.	*Crocker Nucl.			
	Lab.	1 1/2 2/3	65	
Los Angeles, Ca	University of			
	California	1 1/2 2/3	22	TCC
Seattle, Wash.	Univ. of			
	Washington	1 1/2 2/3	48	Scanditronix

Table 7 (continued)
CYCLOTRONS WITH FACILITIES FOR RADIONUCLIDE PRODUCTION[a]

Location	Institution	e/m of accelerated particles[b]	Maximum energy (for p)/MeV	Manufacturer[c]
St. Louis, Mo.	Washington Univ. Med. School *Mallinckrodt	1 1/2 2/3	15	TCC
	Chem. Works	1	42	TCC
USSR:				
Alma Ata	Inst. Nucl. Phys.	1 1/2 2/3	30	
Venezuela:				
Caracas	Universidad Simón Bolivar	?		

[a] Data up to 1978 from Reference 207.
[b] e/m = 1:p, e/m = 1/2: d,α, e/m = 2/3:^{3}He^{++}.
[c] TCC = The Cyclotron Corporation, CGR = CGR-MeV.
[d] Proposal.
[e] Under construction or being delivered.
[f] By upgrading the old cyclotron.

Note: Large-scale producers of radionuclides running their cyclotrons exclusively for this purpose or alternatively joining a commercialized distribution system have been marked by an asterisk in the second column.

quencies are of the order of 10 MHz, amplitudes about 30 to 50 keV to ground. Alignment of the electrodes between the pole tips of a constant magnetic field contains the particles to near circular orbits within the electrodes (see Figure 20).

The basic equation of motion is derived from the condition, that a particle of charge e and velocity v = $\omega \cdot$ r (ω = angular velocity) moving on a trajectory of radius r in a magnetic field B experiences a Lorentz force evB which is balanced by the centrifugual force $mv^2/r = m\omega^2r$:

$$mv^2/r = evB \tag{9}$$

So, particles have the angular velocity

$$\omega = v/r = (e/m)B \tag{10}$$

which is apparently independent on v (or the energy) and the radius of the orbit. Within certain limits, imposed by the relativistic mass increase and focusing conditions, particles can thus be accelerated in a constant magnetic field by an alternating electric field of fixed frequency f = $\omega/2\pi$ which just in time switches the downstream dee to negative polarity so that the ions always perceive an attractive force when traversing the accelerating gap. Extraction of the ions from the magnet is managed by the combined action of a curved electrical field (deflector) and the magnetic fringing field.

In powerful compact cyclotrons, the process of extraction must be strongly supported by a small perturbation of the magnetic field (''field bump'') causing a precession of the orbits such that their separation at the deflector entrance is wide enough to protect the grounded inner electrode (''septum'') from too high a heat dissipation by the peeled-off beam. It is a prove for the skill of the cyclotron designer to provide for a proper field bump and of the

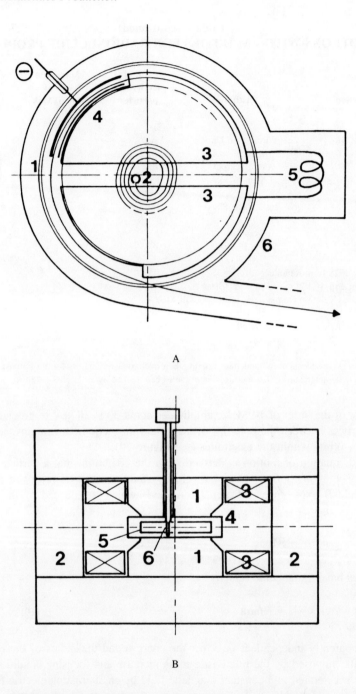

FIGURE 20.   The workings of a cyclotron: (A) acceleration (horizontal cross-
sectional) and (B) main components (vertical cross-sectional).

operating team to profit from it for optimizing extraction efficiency and extracted beam
current.

Equation 10 is called the cyclotron resonance frequency condition. The energy of an
orbiting particle being $E = \theta\ \omega^2/2$ with the moment of inertia $\Theta = mr^2$ in this case, we
get:

$$E = mr^2 (eB/m)^2/2 = (r^2B^2/2) e^2/m = K e^2/m \qquad (11)$$

with the so-called K-value $r^2B^2/2$ (r measured in mtr and B in kilo-Gauss) which is the characteristic feature of a cyclotron.

We see that the energy is proportional to $e^2(\text{or}(ze)^2$ if $z > 1)$, to B^2, and r^2. As one always uses the maximum possible B, the correlation between r and E turns out to be:

$$r = \text{const.} \sqrt{E}$$

or doubling the energy of a special particle ($e/m = \text{const.}$) is in practice accomplished by increasing r by the factor $\sqrt{2}$. (As a consequence, the cross-section of the cyclotron magnet and hence its weight — and price — is roughly proportional to r^2 or E).

For example, we note that 20 MeV protons (or 10 MeV deuterons: $(e^2/m)_d = (1/2) (e^2/m)_p$, or 20 MeV α-particles: $(Z^2e^2/m_\alpha = (e^2/m)_p$ for $Z = 2$) can be supplied by a cyclotron of about 1 m cross-section of the pole faces ($r_{extr} \approx 0.45$ m) with an (average) magnetic field $\overline{B} = 1.5$ Tesla $= 15$ Kilo Gauss ($K = r^2B^2/2 = 0.45^2 \times 15^2/2 = 22$) and an orbital frequency of about 10 MHz, i.e., radiofrequencies of 10, 20, 30, etc., MHz depending on the "mode" of acceleration.

At 20 MeV, the relativistic mass increase for protons is: $(m - m_0)/m_0 = (1 - v^2/c^2)^{-1/2} - 1 = (1/2) (v/c)^2 = E/m_pc^2 = 20 \text{ MeV}/938 \text{ MeV} \cong 2\%$. It is already noticeable and has to be allowed for by a magnetic field shape accordingly increasing with the radius of the orbit.

For a more elaborate study of the delicate problems of beam dynamics, magnetic field profile, focusing conditions, phase space, and extraction, we refer to the special literature.[108]

Up to the early 1960s, cyclotrons have been built by the groups who intended to work them. This is still true for big machines or advanced designs disposed to basic physics research (elementary particles, heavy ions) and accelerator development. Smaller ("compact") cyclotrons for mainly biomedical applications, i.e., radionuclide production, high-LET radiation therapy and biology, activation analysis, etc., are now available from three manufacturers.*

From the reasons of maximum radionuclide yield and proper depth dose for fast neutrons in tissue an energy of the extracted beam of about 40 to 50 MeV (for $e^2/mm = 1$-particles) is regarded as adequate today. Extracted beam currents of more than 100 μA have been achieved. Many institutions, scientific, medical, and commercial have installed compact cyclotrons of this caliber since 1977, a few centers are operating cyclotrons up to 90 MeV for the applications mentioned or intend to do so. Table 1 provides a summary of cyclotron installations being used at least in part as "radionuclide factories".

Accelerator centers with very high ion energies (> 100 MeV) recently tried to use their beam right before the "dump" for spallation reactions (p,xn,. . .) with $x \geqslant 1$. At such energies, however, the excitation functions of many concurring reactions approach each other, and, consequently, the product can be appreciably contaminated by radionuclides of varying neutron number (and hence identical chemical behavior). Appropriate separation is only possible, if half-lives are sufficiently different. So, this technique has not experienced widespread use today with the exception of the reactions $^{127}I(p,xn)Xe$ or $^{127}I(d,xn)Xe$ already mentioned,[58,109] working, however, at the lower end of this energy range.

B. The Resonant Linear Accelerator (LINAC)

Realized at first by Wideröe in 1928, soon afterwards in a more advanced layout achieving

---

* The Cyclotron Corporation, Berkeley, California, USA; CGR-MeV, Buc (near Paris), France; Scanditronix, Uppsala, Sweden.

ion energies above 1 MeV by Sloan and Lawrence (Berkeley 1930), the "resonant" LINAC is based on the principle of repeated acceleration of charged particles in high frequency electric fields by crossing the gaps between successive "drift tubes" mounted on the axis of a highly evacuated cylindrical tank. The tubes are either coupled to high frequency generators or, if the tank itself is used as a resonator ("Alvarez-type"[110]), their alternating potentials are provided by the standing wave in it. The particles have to pass each gap just at that moment, when the electric field is switched into the accelerating direction. Between these periods, the drift tubes act as electrical shields. So, a net energy gain is achieved for drift tubes have to increase due to the growing velocity of the particles, because the frequency is fixed from geometrical reasons. To limit the design problems arising from very different tube lengths, particles are injected with appreciable energies (several hundred kV) by another small "potential-drop" linear accelerator. As the peak voltage per gap is limited (by sparking), the number of gaps and the length of the accelerator soon reaches huge dimensions. So does the high frequency power required to establish the desired field strength and to overcome the unavoidable energy dissipation in the resonator. For a resonant circuit of capacity C, and quality factor Q operating at a frequency f with an effective voltage amplitude V, the electrical power dissipation amounts to

$$P = V^2 C \, 2\pi f / Q$$

which is needed for every gap of the system. For example, we take $V = 200$ kV, $C = 10$ pF, $f = 20$ MHz, and $Q = 1000$, for a high quality resonator. Hence, $P = (2 \cdot 10^5 V)^2 \cdot 10 \cdot 10^{-12} F \cdot 2\pi \cdot 20 \cdot 10^6 sec^{-1}/10^3 = 50$ kilowatts (with 1 F = 1 A sec/V) needed to maintain the high frequency amplitude at one gap. These figures quickly add up to several megawatts, far above the power consumption of a cyclotron. From this reason dynamic LINACs have developed strongly only after World War II with its heavy impact on high frequency and microwave technology (RADAR).

The outstanding quality of the extracted beams determined this type of accelerator primarily as an injector for high energy synchrotons with their extraordinary requirements in beam acceptance. For a more detailed study of LINAC design and related problems, see Reference 112.

Only very few are being used for radionuclide production: The Brookhaven Linear Isotope Producer (BLIP) at Brookhaven National Laboratory, Upton, N.Y.[111] and a very recent design built exclusively for this purpose by New England Nuclear, N. Billerica, Mass. (see Table 8) which delivers an ion current about two orders of magnitude higher than a modern compact cyclotron.

C. Nuclear Fission Reactor

Due to its high neutron fluence rate, its stable operation and the ease of sample handling the slow, water-moderated fission research reactor (shortly "reactor") has turned out to be the most efficient particle source for neutron-induced nuclear reactions. Among all reactor models existing, the "swimming pool" type is best suited to introduce the irradiation equipment used in radionuclide production, neutron activation analysis, dosimetry, and material testing.

In a reactor of the considered design, neutrons are produced by fission of ^{235}U: after absorption of a slow neutron the two ^{235}U nucleus disintegrates into two medium heavy nuclei and two to three energetic neutrons, the mass defect of 195 MeV per fission being expressed as kinetic energy and excitation of the fragments. After slowing down ("moderation") of the neutrons by collisions with the surrounding moderator material (usually water), a reaction chain is maintained if at least one of the neutrons is left to hit the next

Table 8
RESONANT LINACS FOR RADIONUCLIDE PRODUCTION

LINAC-design	BLIP	NEN
Particles	p	p
Energy(MeV)	50	45
Beam current(mA)	50/puls	5
No. of gaps		100
Frequency(MHz)	201	200
Length(m)	35	25,6
Power consumption(MW)	5	5
Injector	Cockcroft-Walton, 750 keV	Cockcroft-Walton, 780 keV

Note: The NEN-LINAC is proposed for producing large activities mainly of the radionuclides ^{201}Tl and ^{67}Ga.

^{235}U nucleus. The uranium, embedded in a rigid matrix with a high melting point (e.g., Zirkonium hydride) is canned in gas-tight metal tubes, the "fuel elements", packed together in a special arrangement ("core") near the bottom of the moderator tank.

At the very beginning, natural uranium was taken as fission material (containing only 0.7% of ^{235}U because the technology of enriching special nuclides in a big scale had not yet been developed. To minimize loss of neutrons by absorption in the moderator material (i.e., by the protons) one then has to take D_2O (heavy water) with its known small neutron absorption cross-section. With enriched ^{235}U (usually some 20%), inexpensive deonized H_2O is being used as a moderator fluid, today.

Irradiation positions to introduce samples for neutron exposure are provided between the fuel rods ("in-core" positions) and in a ring ("lazy susan") rotating slowly round the core within the enclosing metal-canned hollow cyclinder made from low-Z material (usually graphite) with very low neutron absorption cross-section. This "reflector" has to scatter back a part of the neutrons escaping from the core and to minimize neutron losses occurring by absorption in the moderator and reactor equipment. It thus helps to save fuel.

Depending on the power output, some 50 to 100 fuel elements are located in the core. The surrounding moderator covering the core by a column of, say, 6 to 8 m has to meet two additional objectives, namely to take away the reaction heat and to shield the radiation, both neutrons and gamma, upward. The moderator tank is located in the "biological shield", a huge cylinder made from (heavy) concrete with walls several meters thick. For more details of reactor design see Reference 113.

Samples usually housed in special plastic containers are introduced and unloaded by a sort of fishing-tackle or, more comfortably and safe, by a pneumatic or water-driven transfer system.[114] Volumes of several hundred of ccm are provided in all irradiation positions, so big quantities of material can be exposed. Extracted neutron beams are not relevant in our context due to their low flux values achieved at the exit port.

The energy spectrum of fission neutrons covers the range from slow neutrons (E = 0.001 eV) up to about 10 MeV with one maximum around 1 to 2 MeV. There is a rough and practical division into three energy groups:

1. Slow (thermal) neutrons: E ≤ 0.2 eV being in thermal equilibrium with the moderator material; medium energy 0.025 eV resulting in a medium velocity v = 2200 m/sec.
2. Epithermal or resonance neutrons: 0.2 eV ≤ E ≤ 0.5 MeV, largely from neutrons slowed down by collisions with the nuclei of the moderator substance.

3.   Fast neutrons: $E > 0.5$ MeV, directly from the fission process. In all three domains, the shapes ψ (E) of the energy distributions can be well approximated by simple analytical functions of E.[113,115] They are verified by activation foil technique.

The neutron flux (or fluence rate) Φ, i.e., the number of neutrons per second crossing a sphere of 1 cm^2 cross-section in all directions, in either group is given by the integral of ψ (E) over the corresponding energy range. In the center of a 250 kW TRIGA-type research reactor, for example, the thermal flux $\Phi_{th} = 10^{13}$ cm^{-2} sec^{-1}, the epithermal $\Phi_{epi} = 10^{12}$ cm^{-2} sec^{-1}, and the fast neutron flux $\Phi_f = 10^{13}$ cm^{-2} sec^{-1}.

The essential figure is given by Φ_{th}, as most clinically used radionuclides are produced via thermal neutron capture. 10^{13}n/cm^{2}sec is the order of magnitude needed to establish sufficient activities, say several milliCuries (after chemical processing).

The activity A (sec^{-1} = Becquerel) of a sample of mass G (grams), atomic weight M (grams), and reaction cross-section σ (cm^2), exposed to a neutron flux Φ (cm^{-2}sec^{-1}) for a time t_1, resulting in a radionuclide of half-life $T_{1/2}$, is given by

$$A = \Theta \cdot \frac{G}{M} \cdot \sigma \, hN_L \, (1 - e^{-\lambda t_1})$$

at the end of bombardment, very similar to Equation 3, with: h = atomic abundance of the starting nuclide; N_L = Avogadro's number; $\lambda = 1n2/T_{1/2}$.

To convert to mCi or Ci, divide by 3.7×10^7 or 3.7×10^{10}, respectively. The maximum attainable value $\Phi\sigma$hLG/M is called saturation activity here, too.

After a time t_2 elapsed after end of exposure the activity has, of course, decayed to

$$A(t_2) = A \cdot e^{-\lambda t_2}$$

The value of Φ appropriate for the reaction in question has to be determined for each irradiation position by measurement. It depends on core geometry and reactor power output. Cross-sections are given for example in References 115 and 116. Activities can then be easily derived from well-prepared tables.[117]

The flux of gamma quanta in a reactor core, being of the order of 50% of the thermal neutron flux Φ_{th}, though not relevant for the activation process, has nevertheless to be taken into some account because it can cause appreciable radiation damage in the sample itself and in the encapsulation.

1. Neutron Generators

The yield from a modern neutron generator tube is of the order of 10^{12}n/cm^{2}sec, and hence the fast neutron flux is around 10^{12}cm^{-2}sec^{-1} at a practical source target distance of about 1 m, far below the capabilities of a fission research reactor. Thus, this type of neutron source is restricted in application to activation analysis, radiation biology, and high-LET radiation therapy.

The principle of operation is based on the d-T fusion reaction T(d,n)^{4}He which has a resonance cross-section of about 7 barns near 150 keV supplying nearly monochromatic fast neutrons around 15 MeV, depending a little on the energy of the deuterons. In a "classical" generator tube deuterons are accelerated by a static electric field provided by a 200 kV rectifier of the Greinacher (or Cockcroft-Walton) type. The ions impinge on a disk of tungsten loaded with tritium. The target is watercooled and sometimes rotated. As the reaction is nearly isotropic only a small fraction of the neutrons can effectively be used if the beam is collimated by a duct through the heavy shield around the assembly. Ion currents are of the order of 100 mA. To increase efficiency small magnetic spectrometers have been introduced into the tubes in order to separate the (inefficient) D_2^+-ions from the deuterons.[118] The tritium in the target disk is used up by the reaction. So, this type of generator provides a neutron flux fading from the beginning, i.e., the source strength is continuously decreasing. The more advanced design called KARIN[119] uses a cylindrical Scandium target loaded with both tritium and deuterium bombarded by deuterons and tritons from a surrounding circular ion source. The tritium-deuterium losses in the target are compensated by the implanted ions. This results in a constant output for several hundred hours before the active ScDT-layer is carried away by sputtering. At 150 kV/150 mA a source strength of $5 \cdot 10^{12}$n/sec has been achieved. A similar design of neutron generator is being developed by The Cyclotron Corporation.

D. Other Neutron Sources

As standards for physical and dosimetric measurements, and teaching compact solid state neutron sources are in use up to now. There are three types:

1. (α, n)-sources emitting a continuous neutron spectrum. They are based on the reaction $^9Be (\alpha,n)^{12}C$ with α-particles from ^{226}Ra and its decay products (Ra-Be-source) from ^{210}Po (Po-Be-source) or from ^{239}Pu (Pu-Be-source). The design consists of a pellet pressed from a mixture of a radium salt with beryllium powder or a Pu-Be-alloy, respectively, housed in a gas-tight capsule within a safe container. Source strengths are of the order of 1.5×10^7 n/sec per gram radium, 2.5×10^6n/sec per Curie of ^{210}Po, and 8.5×10^4n/sec per gram ^{239}Pu, respectively.
2. (γ,n)-sources, using the nuclear photo disintegration of deuterium or beryllium by γ-emitters like ^{124}Sb, ^{88}Y and others. They deliver monoenergetic neutrons. The yield is one to three orders of magnitude lower relative to 1 Curie of operating activity.
3. Fission-neutron-sources: ^{252}Cf, ^{240}Pu, and other heavy radionuclides decay by spontaneous fission releasing neutrons with the continuous fission energy spectrum. ^{252}Cf has attained significance in interstitial high-LET radiotherapy.

A more elaborate description and special references are to be found in Reference 113.

All other sources of heavy particles, electrons, and photons interesting in design and application shall be omitted here because they are not meaningful within the scope of this representation.

REFERENCES

1. **Browne, E., Dairiki, J. M., and Doebler, R. E.,** *Table of Isotopes,* 7th ed., John Wiley & Sons, New York, 1978.
2. **Walker, F. E., Kirouac, G. J., and Rourke, F. M.,** *Chart of Nuclides,* 12th ed., U.S. Dept. of Energy, Schenectady, NY, 1977.
3. **Joliot, F. and Curie, I.,** *Nature (London),* 10, 201, 1934.
4. **Rutherford, E., Chadwick, J., and Ellis, C. D.,** *Radiation From Radioactive Substances,* Cambridge University Press, Cambridge, Mass., 1930.
5. **Casper, J.,** *Ann. N.Y. Acad. Sci.,* 145, 527, 1967.
6. **Paneth, F. and Hevesy, G.,** *Monatsh. Chemie,* 34, 1401, 1913.
7. **Becquerel, H.,** *C. R. Acad. Sci. Paris,* 122, 501, 1896.
8. **Rutherford, E.,** *Philos. Mag.,* 37, 581, 1919.

9. **Sloan, D. H. and Lawrence, E. Phys. Rev.,** 38, 2021, 1931.
10. **Lawrence, E. O.,** *Phys. Rev.,* 46, 746, 1934.
11. **Smyth, H. D.,** *Atomic Energy for Military Use,* 1945.
12. **Szilard, L. and Chalmers, T. A.,** *Nature (London),* 134, 462, 1934.
13. **Bohr, N. and Wheeler, J. A.,** *Phys. Rev.,* 56, 426, 1939.
14. **Katcoff, S.,** *Nucleonics,* 18(11), 201, 1960.
15. **Richards, P.,** $^{99}\Sigma$Tc generator, in Radioactive Pharmaceuticals, Symp. No. 6, CONF 651111, U.S. Atomic Energy Commission, Oak Ridge, TN, 1966, 323.
16. **Livingstone, M. S. and Blewett, I. P.,** *Particle Accelerators,* McGraw-Hill, New York, 1962.
17. **Silvester, D. J. and Waters, S.,** Second International Symposium on Radiopharmaceuticals, March 19-22, 1979, Seattle, WA.
18. **Barschall, H. H.,** *Ann. Rev. Nucl. Sci.,* 28, 207, 1978.
19. **Richards, P.,** Nuclide generators, in Radioactive Pharmaceuticals, Symp. No. 6, CONF 651111, U.S. Atomic Energy Commission, Oak Ridge, TN, 1969.
20. **Brucer, M.,** *Isotope Radiat. Technol.,* 3, 1, 1965.
21. **Stang, L. G., Jr.,** Radionuclide Generators, Past, Present, and Future, BNL Rep. No. 13595, CONF 690413-1, U.S. Atomic Energy Commission, Oak Ridge, TN, 1969.
22. **Stetten, D., Jr.,** *Science,* 185, 1974.
23. **Helus, F. and Maier-Borst, W.,** Neunte Jahrestagung der Gessellschaft fur Nuklearmedizin, *Nuklearmedizin,* 336, 1973.
24. **Chan, P. K. H., Firnau, G., and Garnett, E. S.,** *Radiochem. Radioanal. Lett.,* 19, 237, 1974.
25. **Firnau, G., Nahmias, C., and Garnett, E. S.,** *Int. J. Appl. Radiat. Isotopes,* 24, 182, 1973.
26. **Goldberg, M. D., Mughabghab, S. F.,** et al., Neutron Cross Sections, Rep. No. BNL-325, Brookhaven National Laboratory, Upton, N.Y., 1966.
27. Radioisotope Production and Quality Control; Technical Rep. No. 128, International Atomic Energy Association, Vienna, 1971, 80.
28. **Beg, K. and Brown, F.,** *Int. J. Appl. Radiat. Isotopes,* 14, 137, 1963.
29. **Thomas, C. C., Jr., Sondel, J. A., and Kerns, R. C.,** *Int. J. Appl. Radiat. Isotopes,* 16, 71, 1965.
30. **Krauss, O., Lorenz, W. J., Maier-Borst, W., and Ostertag, H.,** *Kerntechnik,* 17, 221, 1975.
31. **Erbs, G., Georgi, P., Kleinhans, S., and Vogt-Moykopf, I.,** Proc. 13th Int. Ann. Meet. Soc. Nucl. Med., Copenhagen, October 10-13, 1975.
32. **Kusaka, Y. and Meinke, W. W.,** Rapid Radiochemical Separations, Nucl. Sci. Ser. Rep. No. NAS-NS-3104, Subcommittee on Radiochemistry, NRC, Washington, D.C., 1961, 1.
33. **Dorfner, K.,** *Ion Exchangers, Properties, and Applications,* Ann Arbor Science Publishers, Ann Arbor, MI, 1972.
34. **Snyder, L. R. and Kirklans, J. J.,** *Introduction to Modern Liquid Chromatography,* John Wiley & Sons, New York, 1974.
35. **Vonberg, D. D., Baker, L. C., Buckingham, P. D., Clark, J. C., Finding, K., Sharp, J., and Silvester, D. J.,** *Uses of Cyclotrons in Chemistry, Metallurgy, and Biology,* Amphlett, C. B., Ed., Butterworths, London, 1970.
36. **Wilson, R. W., and Kamen, M. D.,** *Phys. Rev.,* 54, 1031, 1938.
37. **Kurie, F. N. D.,** *Rev. Sci. Instr.,* 10, 199, 1939.
38. **Martin, J. A., Livingstone, R. S., Murray, R. L., and Rankin, M.,** *Nucleonics,* 13, 28, 1955.
39. **Martin, J. A. and Green, F. L.,** *Nucl. Sci. Eng.,* 1, 185, 1956.
40. **Kobisk, E.,** *Nucleonics,* 24, 122, 1966.
41. **Crouzel, C., Le Poec, C., Jarry, E., Knipper, R., and Comar, D.,** *Nucl. Inst. Meth.,* 165, 341, 1979.
42. **Wieland, B. W., Highfill, R. R., and King, P. H.,** *IEEE Trans. Nucl Sci.,* 1, 1713, 1979.
43. **Clark, J. C., Goulding, R. W., Roman, M., and Palmer, A. J.,** *Radiochem. Radioanal. Lett.,* 14, 101, 1973.
44. **Acerbi, E., Birattari, C., Bonardi, M., de Martins, C., and Salomone, A.,** *Int. J. Appl. Radiat. Isotopes,* 32, 465, 1981.
45. **Buchanan, J. M. and Hastings, A. B.,** *Phys. Rev.,* 26, 120, 1946.
46. **Kamen, M. D.,** Short-lived radioactive carbon — ^{11}C, in *Radioactive Tracers in Biology,* 2nd ed., Academic Press, New York, 1951, chap. 8.
47. **Buckingham, P. D. and Forse, G. R.,** *Int. J. Appl. Radiat. Isotopes,* 14, 439, 1963.
48. Proc. May 19-20, Conf. Applications of ^{123}I in Nuclear Medicine, 1975, U.S. Dept. of Health, Education and Welfare Rep. No. FDA-76-8022, Rockville, MD, 1976.
49. **Qaim, S. M., Stöcklin, G., and Weinreich, R.,** Proc. of Panel Discussion on ^{123}I in Western Europe, KFA Julich, Fed. Rep. Germany, February 13, 1976.
50. **Sodd, V. J., Schulz, K. L., Blau, J. W., and Wellman, H. N.,** Public Health Service Publ. No. BRH/DMRE 70-4, U.S. Dept. of Health, Education and Welfare, 1970.

51. Acerbi, E., Biratarri, M., Castiglioni, M., Resmini, M., and Villa, M., *Int. J. Appl. Radiat. Isotopes*, 26, 741, 1975.
52. Kondo, K., Lambrecht, R. M., and Wolf, A. P., *Int. J. Appl. Radiat. Isotopes*, 28, 395, 1977.
53. Van den Bosch, R., De Goeij, J. J. M., Van der Heide, J. A., Tertoolen, J. F. W., Theelen, H. M. J., and Zegers, C., *Int. J. Appl. Radiat. Isotopes*, 28, 255, 1977.
54. Asmus, K. H., Jager, K., Schutz, R., Schulz, F., and Schweickert, H., Proc. 8th Cyclotron Conf., Bloomington, Ind., *IEEE Trans. Nucl Sci.*, 2, 2265, 1979.
55. Lambrecht, R. M. and Wolf, A. P., *Radiat. Res.*, 52, 32, 1972.
56. Lebowitz, E., Greene, M. W., and Richards, P., *Int. J. Appl. Radiat. Isotopes*, 22, 489, 1971.
57. Myers, W. G., *Progress in Atomic Medicine*, Vol. 4, Lawrence, J. H., Ed., Grune & Stratton, New York, 1974.
58. Fusco, M. A., et al., *J. Nucl Med.*, 13, 729, 1972; Weinreich, R., Schult, O., and Stöcklin, G., *Int. J. Appl. Radiat. Isotopes*, 25, 535, 1974.
59. Clark, J. C. and Buckingham, P. D., *Short-Lived Radioactive Gases for Clinical Use*, Butterworths, London, 1975.
60. Welch, M. J. and Ter-Pogossian, M. M., *Radiat. Res.*, 36, 580, 1968.
61. Clark, J. C. and Silvester, D. J., *Int. J. Appl. Radiat. Isotopes*, 17, 151, 1966.
62. Tilbury, R. S., Mamacos, J. P., and Laughlin, J. S., *Uses of Cyclotrons in Chemistry, Metallurgy, and Biology*, Butterworths, London, 1970, 119.
63. Lindner, L., Suer, T. H. G. A., Brinkman, G. A., and Veenboer, J., *Int. J. Appl. Radiat. Isotopes*, 24, 124, 1973.
64. Helus, F., Gaspar, H., Sahm, U., and Maier-Borst, W., *Radiochem. Radioanal. Lett.*, 44, 187, 1980.
65. Carlson, J. D., *Nucl Inst. Meth.*, 113, 541, 1973.
66. Wolf, A. P. and Redwanly, C. S., *Int. J. Appl. Radiat. Isotopes*, 28, 29, 1977.
67. Finn, R. D., Christman, D. R., Ache, H. J., and Wolf, A. P., *Int. J. Appl. Radiat. Isotopes*, 22, 736, 1971.
68. Hanser, A. and Feurer, B., *Int. J. Appl. Radiat. Isotopes*, 32, 775, 1981.
69. Gindler, J. E., Oselka, M. C., Friedman, A. M., Mayron, L. W., and Kaplan, E., *Int. J. Appl. Radiat. Isotopes*, 27, 330, 1976.
70. Oselka, M., Gindler, J. E., and Friedman, A. M., *Int. J. Appl. Radiat. Isotopes*, 28, 804, 1977.
71. McDaniels, D. K., Bergquist, I., Drak, D., and Martin, J. T., *Nucl. Inst. Meth.*, 99, 77, 1972.
72. Zemansky, M. W., *Heat and Thermodynamics*, McGraw-Hill, New York, 1951, 83.
73. Del Fiore, G., Depresseux, J. C., Bartsch, P., Quaglia, L., and Peters, J. M., *Nucl Inst. Meth.*, 163, 479, 1979.
74. Peters, J. M., Del Fiore, G., Quaglia, L., Depresseux, J. C., and Bartsch, P., *Nucl Inst. Meth.*, 165, 157, 1979.
75. Filss, P., Guldbakke, S., Nolte, G., and Tietze, K., *Nucl Inst. Meth.*, 91, 1, 1971.
76. Hichwa, R. D. and Nickles, R. J., *IEEE Trans. Nucl. Sci.*, 26, 1707, 1979.
77. Martin, J. A. and Green, F. L., *Nucl. Sci. Eng.*, 1, 185, 1956.
78. Schulz, F. and Bellemann, H., Ein Target fur Hochstrom-bestrahlungen im Zyklotron, Kernforschungszentrum Karlsruhe, KFK-685, Bericht, Dez., 1967.
79. Krasnov, N. N., et al., *Uses of Cyclotrons in Chemistry, Metallurgy, and Biology*, Amphlett, C. B., Ed., Butterworths, London, 1970, 266.
80. Svoboda, K., Hruby, J., and Hradil, M., *Isotopenpraxis*, 3, 313, 1967.
81. Friedman, A. M. and Mohr, W. C., *Nucl. Inst. Meth.*, 17, 78, 1962.
82. von Witsch, W. and Willaschek, J. G., *Nucl Inst. Meth.*, 138, 13, 1976.
83. Clarke, N. M., *Nucl. Inst. Meth.*, 96, 497, 1971.
84. Morris, C. L. and Thornton, S. T., *Nucl Inst. Meth.*, 96, 281, 1971.
85. Porter, L. E., McIntyre, L. C., and Haberli, W., *Nucl Inst. Meth.*, 89, 237, 1970.
86. Burton, G., *Cyclotron Beam Sharing for Multiple Irradiations*, McIlroy, R. W., Ed., Butterworths, London, 1970, 250.
87. Greene, M. W. and Lebowitz, E., *Int. J. Appl. Radiat. Isotopes*, 23, 342, 1972.
88. Watson, I. A., Waters, S. L., Bewley, D. K., and Silvester, D. J., *Nucl. Inst. Meth.*, 106, 231, 1973.
89. Rautenbach, W. I., Steyn, J., Richards, D., and Smith, H. J., *Uses of Cyclotrons in Chemistry, Metallurgy, and Biology*, Amphlett, C. B., Ed., Butterworths, London, 1970, 365.
90. Vaalburg, W., Beerling-van der Molen, H. D., Reiffers, S., Rijskamp, A., Woldring, M. G., and Wynberg, H., *Int. J. Appl. Radiat. Isotopes*, 27, 153, 1976.
91. Strang, R. M. and Ritter, R. C., *Nucl. Inst. Meth.*, 93, 221, 1971.
92. Cunningham, J. G., Morris, B., Nichols, A. L., and Taylor, N. K., *Int. J. Appl. Radiat. Isotopes*, 27, 597, 1976.
93. Fabian, H., *Kerntechnik*, 13, 176, 1971.

94. **Feldl, E. J.**, *Nucl Inst. Meth.*, 117, 5, 1974.
95. **Nolan, P. J., Lister, C. J., and James, A. N.**, *Nucl Inst. Meth.*, 167, 17, 1979.
96. **Chuang, L. S., Shima, K., Ebihara, H., Seki, R., and Mikumo, T.**, *Nucl Inst. Meth.*, 171, 207, 1980.
97. **Barbier, M.**, *Induced Radioactivity*, North-Holland, New York, 1969.
98. **Evans, R. D.**, *The Atomic Nucleus*, McGraw-Hill, New York, 1970.
99. **Wapstra, A. H. and Grove, N. B.**, Nuclear Data Tables, Vol. 9, Springer-Verlag, Heidelberg, 1970; Ans-Lax, D., *Taschenbuch fur Chemiker und Physiker*, Vol. 3, Schäfer, K. and Synowietz, C., Eds., Springer-Verlag, Heidelberg, 1970.
100. **Northcliffe, L. C. and Shilling, R. F.**, Range and stopping power tables for heavy ions, in *Nuclear Data Tables*, Vol 7, Springer-Verlag, Heidelberg, 1970; Williamson, C. F., et al., Tables of Range and Stopping Powers of Chemical Elements for Charged Particles of Energy 0.5 to 500 MeV, CEA-R 3042 Report. Commissariat de l'Energy Atomique, Centre d'Etudes Nucleaires, Saclay, Essone, 1966.
101. **Burke, W. H., et al.**, *Phys. Rev.*, 93, 188, 1954.
102. **Wohlleben, K. and Schuster, E.**, *Radiochim. Acta*, 12, 75, 1969.
103. **Livingstone, M. S. and Bethe, H. A.**, *Rev. Med. Phys.*, 9, 245, 1937; Fano, U., *Ann. Rev. Nucl. Sci.*, 13, 1, 1963.
104. **Zaidins, C. S.**, *Nucl. Inst. Met Meth.*, 158, 237, 1979.
105. **Keller, K. A., Lange, J., and Münzel, H.**, Q-values and excitation functions for nuclear reactions, in *Landolt-Börnstein New Series Group I*, Vol. 5, Schopper, H., Ed., Springer-Verlag, New York, 1973.
106. **Lawrence, E. O. and Livingstone, M. S.**, *Phys. Rev.*, 40, 19, 1932.
107. **Martin, J. A.**, Cyclotrons 1978, *IEEE Trans. Nucl. Sci.*, 26, 1979.
108. **Livingood, J. J.**, *Cyclic Particle Accelerators*, Van Nostrand, New York, 1961; Kollath, R., Teilchen-beschleuniger, Vieweg, Braunschweig, 1962; Schulte, W. M., *Nucl. Inst. Meth.*, 171, 409, 1980.
109. **Weinreich, R., Schult, O., and Stocklin, G.**, *Int. J. Appl. Radiat. Isotopes*, 25, 535, 1974.
110. **Alvarez, L. W.**, *Phys. Rev.*, 70, 799, 1946.
111. **Servian, J. L.**, *Int. J. Appl. Radiat. Isotopes*, 26, 763, 1975.
112. **Livingstone, M. S.**, *High Energy Accelerators*, Interscience, New York, 1954.
113. **Beckurts, K. H. and Wirtz, K.**, *Neutron Physics*, Springer-Verlag, New York, 1964.
114. **Lorenz, W. J.**, Radionuklidproduktion mit Forschungsreaktoren fur medizinisch-biologischen Anwendungen, in *Encyclopedia of Medical Radiology*, Diethelm, L., Ed., Springer-Verlag, Heidelberg, 1980.
115. **Glasstone, S. and Eklund, M. C.**, *The Elements of Nuclear Reactor Theory*, van Nostrand, Princeton, 1952; Reactor Physics Constants, Rep. No. ANL-5800, USAC Argonne National Laboratory, Argonne, Ill., 1973.
116. **Liesken, H. and Paulsen, A.**, *Compilation of Cross Sections for some Neutron Induced Threshold Reactions*, Presses Academiques Europeennes, Brussels, 1966.
117. **Baumgartner, F.**, *Table of Neutron Activation Constants*, Thiemig Verlag, Munchen, 1967.
118. **Hess, A. and Franke, H. D.**, *Strahlentherapie*, 155, 486, 1979.
119. **Schmidt, K. A. and Dormann, H.**, *Atomkernenergie*, 27, 159, 1976.
120. **Helus, F., Maier-Borst, W., Sahm, U., and Wiebe, L. I.**, *Radiochem. Radioanal. Lett.*, 38, 395, 1979.
121. **Mladjenovic, M.**, *Radioisotope and Radiation Physics*, Academic Press, New York, 1973, 94.
122. **Shuhmacher, B. W.**, A review of the laws for electron penetration through matter, in *Electron and Ion Beam Science and Technology*, Bakish, P., Ed., John Wiley & Sons, New York, 1965.

Chapter 4

RADIOCHEMICAL PROCESSING OF ACTIVATED TARGETS

G. D. Robinson, Jr.

TABLE OF CONTENTS

I. INTRODUCTION

The processing of activated targets involves the various aspects of purifying and isolating radionuclides after their production by a nuclear reaction. This aspect of radionuclide production is, of course, central to providing radionuclides for use in chemical, physical, biological, and medical studies. The selection or development of an appropriate processing method is affected by several, sometimes interrelated, factors. Nuclear and radiochemical considerations are largely determined by the nature of the target material, the activation process, and the chemical identity of the product radionuclide. The chemical separation and isolation process is designed to permit recovery of the purified radionuclide in a form which is suitable for its intended application. The application may, in fact, impose severe limits on the acceptable limits of chemical, radiochemical, and radionuclidic purity. Finally, the processing must be done reliably and safely, even when a very large quantity of radionuclide is involved. These interactions are illustrated in the block diagram in Figure 1.

Within the constraints imposed by the factors outlined above, the development of a suitable radiochemical processing method focuses upon: (1) separating the product radionuclide from the bulk target material; (2) removing unwanted traces of chemical and radionuclidic impurities; and (3) recovering the product radionuclide in a suitable chemical form and concentration.

It is not our intention to cover in great detail the tremendous amount of work on radionuclide production and processing which has been done and published in various journals, monographs, symposia proceedings, textbooks, etc. Most of the more valuable reference works are listed in the reference list or are cited throughout the text of this manuscript. Although the information found in such reviews may be in insufficient detail by itself, such references still offer access to the many primary literature reports where procedures are described in precise detail.

It is useful to point out that, while newer, more efficient, more reliable, and faster procedures continue to be developed and to appear in the current literature, the older references still serve as useful sources of information on procedures and techniques which can often be easily adapted to meet an immediate need. It is almost always simpler, easier, and more cost effective to modify an existing technique or method than it is to develop an entirely new one, although this is not always possible.

II. NUCLEAR AND RADIOCHEMISTRY

The type and operating characteristics of available nuclear facilities place limits on the nuclear reactions which are possible choices for use in radionuclide production. These considerations restrict target choice and design, which in turn restricts the chemical approaches which will be suitable for processing. If accelerator production is contemplated, the types of particle beams which are available, their energies and beam currents, are taken into account. In a reactor facility, the available thermal and fast neutron fluxes, both in steady-state and pulsed modes, are considered.

Fortunately, as was previously noted, once the intended application is known, and the mode of radionuclide production is chosen, a great deal of information in the form of literature references and other accounts of previous work is available. The methods and techniques which are used for radiochemical processing of activated targets are often surprisingly independent of the type of nuclear reaction used for radionuclide production. Rather, the processing methodologies focus on the chemical differences, or similarities, between the target and the product radionuclide or nuclides. Many of the processing schemes which are now used for isolating accelerator produced radionuclides are directly derived from methods

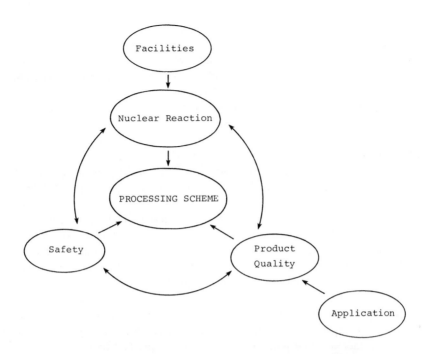

FIGURE 1. Interrelation between factors in the selection or development of an "appropriate" radiochemical processing scheme.

which were originally developed for reactor production applications. For example, the distillation methods which are used for separation of ^{123}I from enriched ^{122}Te or ^{124}Te targets represent modification of the procedures which were originally developed for separation of neutron activation produced ^{131}I from the Te target.[1-5] Likewise, many of the well-developed radiochemical processing methods for the transition metals, such as Cu from Zn, In from Cd, Mn from Fe, etc., can be used equally well with accelerator or reactor-produced radionuclides.[6-8] This applies even more so to processes developed for fission products or when the (n,p) or (n,α) routes for reactor production are involved.

Although the chemistry used in processing activated targets usually depends simply upon the nature of the target material and product radionuclide, one important difference between accelerator and reactor products is often encountered. In reactor production by thermal neutron activation, the (n,γ) process, the product radionuclide is isotopic with the target itself, since no net change in Z (the number of nuclear protons) occurs. Unless some special provision has been made to take advantage of the chemical effects of the nuclear transformation,[9-12] the target material and product radionuclide are chemically indistinguishable. With accelerator processes, since a net change in Z usually accompanies the nuclear reaction, the target and product represent different elements and are relatively easy to separate by conventional chemical means. Production and isolation of radionuclides at very high specific activities are usually more easily achieved with accelerator production or as a result of fission if a reactor is used. Once again, an exception are those nuclear reactions which are induced by "fast" neutrons and result in nonisotopic products. The $^{32}S(n,p)^{32}P$ and $^{27}Al(n,α)^{24}Na$ reactions are examples of such nuclear production routes.

III. RADIOCHEMICAL SEPARATIONS

Regardless of the mode of radionuclide production, the radiochemical processing scheme invariably consists essentially of one or more of the conventional chemical separation methods, such as distillation, extraction, precipitation, or chromatography, which has been adapted to satisfy the unique requirements which are imposed when large amounts of radioactivity are involved. The speed with which such separations must be performed depends most importantly upon the half-life of the product radionuclide. A great deal of effort has gone into the development of separation methods which are suitable for use when ultrashort-lived radionuclides are to be processed.[13]

A. Precipitation

Separations which are based upon precipitation techniques rely upon the different solubilities of the target and product radionuclide in a selected solvent system. While this type of purification step may be used at any stage of target processing, precipitation is most frequently used early on to reduce the total mass of material which must be manipulated in subsequent operations. Most commonly the target material, which is present in the greatest mass, is precipitated out and removed by filtration or centrifugation while the product radionuclide remains in solution. When a sufficient mass of the radioactive element is present, or when a nonisotopic carrier has been added, the product radionuclide can be precipitated and removed from solution. While precipitation techniques are quite useful for removing the large mass of target material from the small quantities of product radionuclide, the selectivities of such separations are often inadequate for achieving required chemical, radiochemical, and radionuclidic purities. In addition, the product radionuclide is often adsorbed upon the surface, or included within the structure of the precipitate, and substantial loss of radioactivity can result. This difficulty is usually most severe when very small masses of product radionuclide are involved, as is the case when high specific activity products are desired. For all of these reasons, simple precipitation alone is rarely adequate to provide a suitable processing scheme.

B. Solvent Extraction

Purification by solvent extraction is based upon the partitioning of solutes between two immiscible solvent phases. This technique has been one of the most widely used methods in the separation of target materials from product radionuclides.[14] Solvent extraction is a relatively simple and rapid technique, which can achieve extreme selectivity. It can be used effectively over a wide range of radionuclide specific activities, and the scale of the process can be adjusted to accomodate widely varying masses of material.

Most frequently the distribution of solutes between aqueous and organic solvents are employed. A classical example of this approach is found in the extraction of elemental halogens into CCl_4 during the processing of radionuclides of Cl, Br, and I.[15] In addition to this rather straightforward approach, the use of simple complexing ions, counter ions, chelating agents, and complexing or chelating organic solvents increases the versatility and selectivity of the method. Such variables as pH, salt concentration, the volumes and composition of solvents, and temperature can also be manipulated to achieve satisfactory separations. Evaporation of volatile solvents or back extraction with an appropriate aqueous phase are commonly used methods for recovery of the product radionuclide.

Because solvent extraction is a relatively simple technique, it can be easily adapted as a remote or even automated operation. This is a very attractive feature when large amounts of radioactivity must be processed repeatedly.

C. Chromatography

Chromatographic separation methods are closely related to the solvent extraction techniques. In both cases, the separation depends upon the different distribution of solutes between two distinct phases. Since the phases move relative to one another during chromatography, a constant reequilibration of the solute partitioning results. When viewed in this perspective, chromatographic separations can be thought of as a form of continuous, multiple extraction. For this reason, the previous brief description of solvent extraction is relevant to this discussion as well.

While essentially all types of chromatographic separations have been applied in one way or another to the processing of activated targets, liquid chromatography has been most frequently used. Systems based upon ion exchange, adsorption, ligand exchange, reverse phase, etc., have been developed. The equipment used can vary from a simple burette, partially packed with ion exchange resin, to a complex, heavily shielded, remotely controlled, self-contained process assembly.

Perhaps the greatest attraction of chromatographic methods lies in the ability to achieve high resolution of closely related chemical species while, at the same time, minimizing direct manipulation of the equipment involved. For example, by proper selection of solvents, many of the transition metal radionuclides can be sequentially stripped off of strong anion exchangers since they form complex anions with chloride ion.[7,8] Subtle changes in solvent composition can dramatically affect the characteristics of such systems. Isolation of product radionuclides at high specific activities can be easily achieved, especially when the product is eluted first and tailing of unwanted impurities into the radionuclide fraction can be avoided. The limited capacity of chromatographic systems can often be expanded by increasing column dimensions if necessary, although larger elution volumes must then be used.

D. Volatilization

Radiochemical processing of activated targets by means of volatilization techniques, such as distillation or sublimation, can be used to advantage in situations where the product radionuclide is a gaseous element, or when it can be readily converted to a volatile derivative. A variety of factors including the vapor pressures of constituents, their respective boiling points, and the physical nature of the target material affect the ease with which separations can be performed and the quality of the product obtained. In certain cases, very impressive separations can be achieved, and little additional processing of the product radionuclide may be required.

The volatility of Xe allows rapid and efficient separation of Xe radionuclides from molten salt targets.[16] Technetium is readily isolated from MoO_3 by sublimation at elevated temperatures in a flowing O_2 stream.[17,18] As was previously mentioned, the distillation of I radionuclides from acidified aqueous solutions is a classical approach to processing activated Te targets.[1-5] The production of ^{11}C as CO or CO_2 by proton or deuteron bombardment of B_2O_3 targets relies upon the convenient recovery of the gaseous products by the use of a sweep gas stream.[19-22] In cases such as these, if high-specific activity products are being processed, where small masses of product material are involved, special care must be taken when using a flowing gas stream to carry over the volatile product. Otherwise, entrainment of unwanted chemical and radionuclidic impurities in the sweep gas may compromise the purity of the final product.

IV. QUALITY CONTROL

What is possible in terms of radionuclide production is limited by the availability of physical facilities. What is appropriate in terms of nuclear reactions and radiochemical processing is almost invariably determined by the intended application. The acceptable levels of radionuclidic, radiochemical, and chemical impurities are limited by consideration of the anticipated use. In addition, the required chemical form, concentration, and specific activity of the product is restricted by this factor. Radionuclides are used in many applications, the details of which are beyond the intended scope of this discussion. In one primary use, however, as labeled compounds in biological and medical studies, the most stringent limits upon acceptable radionuclidic, radiochemical, and chemical purity are encountered.[23-25]

A. Radionuclidic Purity

The radionuclidic purity of a sample is defined as the fraction of the overall disintegration rate which results from decay of the specified radionuclide. Thus, if a radionuclidic purity of 97% ^{67}Ga and 3% ^{66}Ga is specified, 97% of the decay rate of the sample will be due to ^{67}Ga, while 3% results from decay of ^{66}Ga. Radionuclidic purity is usually measured by using a calibrated solid state counting system coupled to a multichannel analyzer for gamma ray spectroscopy. Detection efficiencies are determined by counting absolute radioactivity standards at a fixed geometry. Radionuclidic purity is calculated by comparing measured photon energies, abundances, and half-lives from the sample with those of published references. Absolute disintegration rates for the various radionuclides which are present in the sample are then derived.

Two types of radionuclidic impurities may be present in the product and it is important to distinguish between them. Radionuclides of elements other than the desired product can usually be reduced to acceptable levels by exploiting chemical differences during development of an appropriate processing scheme. Radionuclides which are isotopic with the product are another matter. Since they are chemically indistinguishable from the product, the levels of these isotopic radionuclidic impurities can be manipulated only by a modification of the nuclear parameters of production or by taking advantage of a difference in half-life and allowing shorter-lived isotopic radionuclides to decay.

High radionuclidic purity is required for products intended for use in almost all biomedical tracer applications. While the specific requirements may vary, consideration of this feature can be quite important. For example, if one wishes to study renal function in animals using ^{123}I-labeled *o*-iodohippuric acid and collimated probe detectors, high radionuclidic purity is required so that only the radioactivity in the detector field of view is registered. Scattered radiation from higher energy impurities, such as ^{124}I, are a potential source of interference in such a study. When imaging studies in humans are used to assess renal function, even higher radionuclidic purity ^{123}I-labeled *o*-iodohippuric acid is required in order to assure the best image resolution, although the patient radiation dose may not be a major consideration because of the short biological half-time of *o*-iodohippuric acid.[26-27] In studies using radioiodinated agents with relatively long biological half-times, such as thyroid or adrenal studies, limits on radionuclidic purity are very high, both in order to obtain high quality images of the distribution of the label and also to minimize radiation dose to the patient.

B. Radiochemical Purity

Radiochemical purity refers to the chemical identity of the specified radionuclide. For example, if 98% of the ^{99m}Tc in a certain preparation is in the form of ^{99m}Tc-DTPA, the radiochemical purity of the sample is said to be 98%, with a radiochemical impurity level of 2%. Radiochemical purity is usually measured by some adaptation of standard analytical technique. While the ease of detecting the activity in the various chemical forms once they have been separated into individual fractions simplifies such determinations, the possibility of altering the composition of high-specific activity preparations during an analysis is a constant concern, and many artifacts associated with such determinations have been described.[28-30]

The need for high radiochemical purity in tracer applications is obvious. Assuming the absence of nonisotopic radionuclide impurities, relatively modest radionuclidic purity may be acceptable if only well counting or simple probe studies are contemplated. On the other hand, the use of a tracer is severely compromised if a significant fraction of the radioactivity is present in an inappropriate chemical form.

This can be of particular concern during the processing of radionuclides which are intended for subsequent use in labeling. In the production of ^{18}F labeled F_2 for use in the synthesis of labeled organic compounds, a large fraction of the ^{18}F activity which is recovered from the target is sometimes found to be in chemical forms other than F_2.[31] Moisture in the systems results in the formation of ^{18}F labeled HF, while the presence of N_2 and CO_2 in the target gas result in the formation of appreciable quantities of ^{18}F labeled NF_3 and CF_4, respectively. The result is that, in cases where large amounts of radiochemical impurities arise, inadequate amounts of ^{18}F labeled F_2 are available for the intended use. In this case, careful attention to detail in conditioning of the target system and in assuring high purity target gas is required. In the processing of radioiodine nuclides by distillation, the product is recovered in dilute NaOH.[1-5] Unless great care is taken, or a reducing agent is added to the alkaline solution, the radioiodine is recovered as a mixture of iodide and iodate. If the subsequent labeling procedure requires iodide as the starting material, the presence of radioiodate will result in lowered radiochemical yields.

In general there are two strategies for resolving problems of radiochemical purity: (1) the radiochemical impurity can be simply removed, or (2) the impurity can be converted into the desired chemical form. If small amounts of impurity are involved they can usually be separated from the product by the types of chemical separations which have been described previously. When a significant amount of the product radionuclide is found to be in the wrong chemical form, it is often more economical to go through a chemical cycle which converts all of the product to the desired form.

C. Chemical Purity

The chemical purity of radioactive products is a reflection of the chemical composition of the sample, with specific emphasis on the amounts of nonradioactive components. The requirements for chemical purity associated with radionuclide production are sometimes less clear than are those for radionuclidic or radiochemical purity. Certainly in some applications, such as the sealed sources used as counting standards, the chemical composition of the product is of little concern. At the other extreme, in radiopharmaceutical preparations which are intended for human use, the most stringent limitations on chemical purity come into effect.

In addition to high radionuclidic and radiochemical purity, radiopharmaceuticals require verification of chemical parameters such as pH, ionic strength, and freedom from toxic and pyrogenic substances, as well as freedom from bacterial contamination. While it may be possible to purify and sterilize the final labeled product after preparation, some special consideration of the unique requirements imposed by this intended use is appropriate. For example, the production of ^{111}In *via* the $^{112}Cd(p,2n)^{111}In$ reaction is frequently used and suitable radiochemical processing schemes have been developed.[32,33] One must consider, however, that Cd is an extremely toxic element, and careful quality control is required to assure that the amount of Cd in the final product solution is low enough for safe use in humans. An alternative approach is to use the $^{109}Ag(\alpha,2n)^{111}In$ production reaction, in which case the presence of a trace amount of Ag, which is significantly less toxic than Cd, in the final product is of less concern.[34]

Another example of the special need for high chemical purity in product radionuclide solutions can be found in the use of the weak chelating agent, 8-hydroxyquinoline, for the labeling of human and animal cells in vitro with ^{67}Ga or ^{111}In. The traces of transition metals which are present in laboratory reagents used during labeling as well as those left over after radiochemical processing can interfere with quantitative formation of the labeled chelate intermediate.[35-37] In this situation, not only must the processing scheme used for production of ^{67}Ga or ^{111}In give a product which is low in total transition metals, but care must be taken to assure that the highest levels of chemical purity in reagents are maintained.

The amount of "carrier", or stable isotopes, present in radiochemical products are of concern for other reasons as well. Very high specific activities may be required for certain applications, such as radioimmunoassays or other competitive binding studies. The use of carrier during processing is precluded in products intended for many such applications. In general, however, the addition of carrier can improve reliability and frequently simplifies the required processing chemistry, such as the addition of iodide during ^{123}I processing by distillation or extraction from Te target solutions.[1-5] In some cases, addition of carrier may be specifically required to provide the product radionuclide in the appropriate chemical form, as in the addition of F_2 for the production of ^{18}F labeled F_2 for use in the synthesis of ^{18}F labeled 5-fluorouracil or 2-deoxy-2-fluoro-D-glucose.[38-40] The production of "carrier free" radionuclides has received a great deal of attention, but recent emphasis has focused upon the difficulties of assuring that a given product is truely free from stable isotopes.[41-42] It is the author's view that carrier-free production is extremely difficult to achieve and is, in fact, impossible to demonstrate. If no carrier has been specifically added during processing, and the amount of stable isotope is analytically undetectable, the designation "no carrier added" is preferred. If the level of carrier is known, the specific activity can then be stated.

V. RADIATION SAFETY

During the course of radionuclide processing, care must be taken to minimize radiation exposure to chemistry personnel. While zero exposure may seem unrealistic, the minimum practically achievable exposure is an appropriate goal. If small amounts of radioactivity are involved this is a simple task. When large amounts of radionuclides are being processed, as is frequently the case in commercial work or in research with short-lived radionuclides for imaging studies, consideration of radiation protection can be a substantial effort.

The traditional approaches to limiting radiation exposure during the handling of radionuclides includes minimizing the time of exposure, maximizing the distance between the source and personnel, and interposing shielding between the source and personnel.

Obviously, the less time one is exposed to a given radiation field the less the amount of radiation dose which will be received. This approach to reducing irradiation of personnel is the least attractive unless very low levels of radioactivity are being handled, as is often the case when a radiochemical processing scheme is first being developed. For example, when verifying the suitability of a certain solvent extraction method for the processing of ^{67}Ga, trace amounts of Ga and Zn radionuclides can be used. In this case some direct handling of the solvent extraction system may be acceptable, although by no means is it to be encouraged. In the production mode, however, when several hundred mCi of ^{67}Ga may be involved, some method of remote manipulation is absolutely essential. In emergency situations such as equipment malfunction or if a spill occurs some direct radiation exposure may be unavoidable. In such cases, the shorter the time of exposure the better!

Since the intensity of a radiation field varies inversely with the square of the distance from the source, the use of remote methods for performing the individual steps in a radiochemical processing scheme is an effective approach to minimizing radiation exposure. There are many methods for achieving remote manipulation of chemical equipment. These range from simple "tongs" or extension handles for operating valves, adding reagents, manipulating activated targets, etc., to sophisticated electromechanical "slave" units, solenoid and pneumatically actuated valves, and the like. In general, once a satisfactory processing sequence has been developed, the entire scheme can be made remote so that no direct interaction, or radiation exposure to the chemist is required. Although many examples of specific systems have appeared in the literature, recent examples include completely remote processing of ^{201}Tl, ^{11}C-methyl iodide and ^{11}C-formaldehyde, and ^{18}F-2-deoxy-2-fluoro-D-glucose.[45-46] Complete automation of many such systems seems feasible and represents the ultimate in remote radiochemical processing.

The unusually strong foundations upon which many radiochemical production facilities are constructed is ample testimony to the amount of lead and other shielding materials which are used for radiation protection. The amount of shielding required depends upon the type and energy of emitted radiation. Simple "shadow shields" are often adequate for shielding physically small sources which are contained in a given location. Shielding of a processing system, in which activity moves from place to place often requires more careful consideration. In this case, the use of specially constructed "hot cells" or lead lined fume hoods can be used to advantage to totally enclose the entire system. Indirect observation through the use of mirrors or TV monitors can be used if progress through a scheme must be determined by visual inspection.

In most radiochemistry laboratories minimum radiation exposure is achieved through a combination of the approaches discussed above. The use of heavily shielded facilities assures that, under normal circumstances, radiation fields to which personnel are directly exposed are near background levels. A close approach to the radioactive source is not possible because of the physical constraints imposed by the shielded structure itself and remote manipulations are therefore used in normal operation. Even with these extensive precautions it is never appropriate to assume that adequate reduction in radiation exposure has been achieved. Frequent monitoring of radiation fields using ionization chamber type survey meters is absolutely essential to verify that radiation levels encountered during radiochemical processing are appropriately low. Monitoring of personnel by use of body, wrist, and finger film badges or other types of dosimeter are also required. An area monitor with an audible alarm is to be recommended so that personnel will become aware immediately if radiation levels reach unacceptably high levels. While such an array of equipment and a personnel monitoring program can be quite expensive, in the final analysis it does not pay to cut corners in this area.

VI. REPRESENTATIVE PROCESSING METHODS

A. Radioiodine

A review of the processing of targets used in the production of radioiodine isotopes will be instructive because it illustrates the application of many of the principles which have been touched upon. Iodine-131 can be produced in a reactor as a result of fission of ^{235}U or by neutron activation of ^{130}Te. In the latter case, the directly produced ^{131}Te rapidly decays to ^{131}I.[47,48] Similarly, in the production of ^{123}I using an accelerator either the ^{124}Te(p,2n)^{123}I or the ^{122}Te(d,n)^{123}I nuclear reaction can be used.[2-5] In the last three nuclear production schemes a tellurium target is used to produce the desired radioiodine product. In all cases, the radiochemical processing methods are remarkably similar.

The processing scheme for the production of ^{131}I by fission of ^{235}U is outlined in Figure 2. Typically, the target consists of a uranium/aluminum alloy. After a delay of several days postirradiation to allow for decay of short-lived radionuclides, radiochemical processing begins by transferring the target to an appropriately shielded facility and dissolving it in 4.5 M NaOH. Provision must be made for trapping the volatile fission products (principally ^{133}Xe) which are liberated during this step. The solution is allowed to cool and stand for several hours while Al(OH)$_3$ precipitates out, carrying much of the unwanted radionuclidic contamination with it. The supernate, which contains the iodine nuclides, is then separated by vacuum filtration. The filtrate is acidified with H$_2$SO$_4$ and transferred to a closed distillation assembly with a water cooled condenser and a trap containing a NaOH/Na$_2$SO$_3$ solution. When heat is applied to the acidified filtrate, radioiodine distills over with water

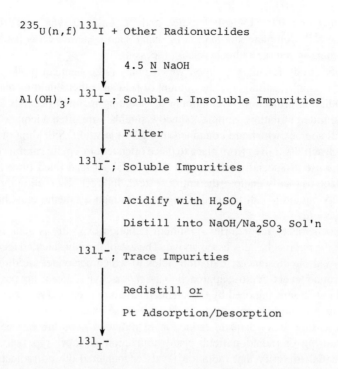

$^{235}U(n,f)$ ^{131}I + Other Radionuclides

|
4.5 $\underline{N}$ NaOH
↓

$Al(OH)_3$; $^{131}I^-$; Soluble + Insoluble Impurities

|
Filter
↓

$^{131}I^-$; Soluble Impurities

|
Acidify with H_2SO_4

Distill into $NaOH/Na_2SO_3$ Sol'n
↓

$^{131}I^-$; Trace Impurities

|
Redistill $\underline{or}$

Pt Adsorption/Desorption
↓

$^{131}I^-$

FIGURE 2.   Distillation processing of ^{131}I after neutron irradiation of ^{235}U in a uranium/aluminum alloy target.

and is collected in the trap as iodide ion. The iodine nuclides distill either as elemental iodine (as a result of air oxidation or from addition of H_2O_2) or as HI. At this point the ^{131}I obtained is not of acceptable radionuclidic purity for most applications, and a redistillation is performed. Alternately, the impure product can be absorbed from an acidified solution onto platinum (sponge or felt). The purified ^{131}I is then recovered by treating the platinum surface with 0.3 *M* NaOH. The pH and concentration of radioactivity in this final solution can then be adjusted as desired. Carrier in the form of fission product ^{127}I and ^{129}I are isolated along with the ^{131}I and so the product is considerably less than carrier free. Nevertheless, using this processing method, a target containing 2.5 g of ^{235}U which is irradiated at a flux of $2 \times 10^{14} n/cm^2$ sec for 4 weeks can yield approximately 100 Ci of high purity ^{131}I.[48]

Iodine-131 which results from decay of ^{131}Te produced by neutron activation of ^{130}Te targets can be processed in a manner quite analogous to the scheme described for fission product ^{131}I. In this case, the target is dissolved in an oxidizing acid solution, such as 6*N* HNO_3 or 18*N* H_2SO_4 and 50% CrO_3(2:1). After dissolution of the target is complete, excess oxidizing agent is destroyed, either chemically or by heat, and the distillation procedes as before. A single distillation is usually sufficient to produce ^{131}I of adequate chemical, radiochemical, and radionuclidic purity for most subsequent applications. If no stable iodine carrier is added during processing, a nearly carrier-free product is obtained. It has been reported that approximately 700 mCi of ^{131}I can be produced per gram of ^{130}Te (99% +) irradiated for 3 weeks at a flux of 2×10^{14} n/cm^2 sec if this procedure is used.[48]

If a natural TeO_2 target is used for production of ^{131}I by the same nuclear reaction sequence, a direct vapor phase processing method has been reported.[49] The target material is heated to 700°C for several hours prior to positioning in the reactor core. This preirradiation heating is used to remove volatile impurities which would be released during postactivation processing. After retrieval of the irradiated TeO_2 target, a sufficient time is allowed for decay

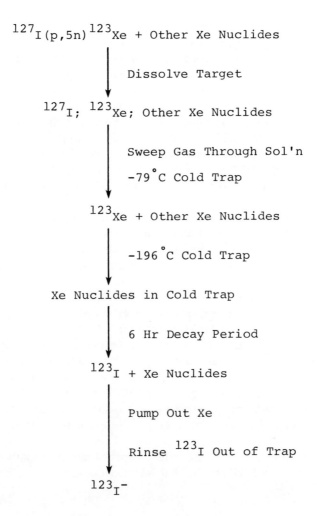

FIGURE 3. Radiochemical processing of ^{123}I after indirect production *via* the [127]Xe(p,5n)[123]Xe(<u>E.C.</u>)[123]I nuclear reaction sequence.

of [131]Te and [131m]Te, and the target is heated to 800°C. A nitrogen gas stream is used to sweep the volatilized ^{131}I into a dilute NaOH trap. Addition of $Na_2S_2O_3$ to the NaOH trap solution assures recovery of ^{131}I-iodide with a radiochemical purity greater than 98%. Microgram quantities of metals such as Pb, Se, and Te are present in the product solution. The advantage of this approach is its great simplicity even though the chemical purity of the product may not be adequate for certain applications.

When radionuclides of the inert gases are produced, volatilization methods are ideally suited to radiochemical processing. As was mentioned previously, the indirect production of ^{123}I via the [127]I(p,5n)[123]Xe(<u>E.C.</u>) [123]I nuclear reaction sequence serves as an example. This is shown schematically in Figure 3. A variety of I-containing materials including NaI, I_2, iodinated organics, etc., have been used as targets.[50-55] As is the case with all (p,5n) reactions, a high energy proton beam is required.

In a typical situation,[50] a target of resublimed, high-purity natural iodine is covered with a thin tantalum foil in a tantalum target assembly. After bombardment with 50 MeV protons, the activated iodine target is dissolved in aqueous KI. A slow stream of He is bubbled through the target solution, the effluent passing successively through cold traps at −79°C (dry ice/acetone) and $-196°C$ (liquid N_2). Water and I_2 are condensed in the first cold trap, and the directly produced Xe isotopes are collected in the second. A 6-hr decay period allows for production of ^{123}I in the second trap. Xenon is removed by warming and evacuating the trap, and the ^{123}I is recovered by rinsing the container with a suitable aqueous solution. Of the variety of Xe isotopes which are produced directly, ^{124}Xe and ^{126}Xe are stable, while ^{122}Xe decays to ^{122}I (3.5 min half-life). Thus only decay of ^{125}Xe to ^{125}I results in radionuclidic contamination of the product. The amount of this radioactive impurity is generally a factor of the time that the Xe radionuclides are allowed to decay during ^{123}I production. Under the conditions described, if a 10 μA proton beam is used for a 3 hr bombardment, a yield of 900 mCi of ^{123}Xe is reported.[50] Sixty mCi of ^{123}I would be available 6 hr after EOB. The ^{125}I level at that time is reported to be 0.1%. Directly produced Te and I isotopes are retained in the $-79°C$ trap.

A variety of accelerator methods for direct production of ^{123}I from enriched tellurium targets have used adaptations of the distillation method for radiochemical processing.[2-5] This is reasonable, because regardless of whether the $^{123}Te(p,n)^{123}I$, $^{124}Te(p,2n)^{123}I$, or $^{122}Te(d,n)^{123}I$ nuclear reactions are used, a similar tellurium/radioiodine separation scheme is involved.

Typically, enriched tellurium powder is packaged in aluminum during the irradiation. After EOB, the target is dissolved by heating in $7M$ H_2SO_4 with addition of an appropriate volume of 30% H_2O_2. During the subsequent distillation, additional H_2O_2 may be added to ensure that the ^{123}I is in a distillable chemical form. Carrier iodine may be added and a nitrogen gas stream may be used to improve transfer into the NaOH trap. If only dilute NaOH is used in the receiving flask, a mixture of ^{123}I-iodide and ^{123}I-iodate is obtained. Addition of a small quantity of reducing agent, such as $Na_2S_2O_3$ or Na_2SO_3, results in a pure ^{123}I-iodide product. Using 200 mg of ^{124}Te (96%) irradiated for 4 hr with 13 μA of 22 MeV protons, production yields of 65 mCi of ^{123}I and 0.45 mCi of ^{124}I (which is formed by the $^{124}Te(p,n)^{124}I$ reaction) were obtained if this distillation based processing scheme was used.[5]

It is appropriate to note that in cases where enriched targets are utilized, the valuable target material is recovered and recycled into additional targets.

B. Carbon-11

Carbon-11 continues to be one of the more widely used accelerator produced radionuclides because of its usefulness as a tracer in relatively simple gaseous forms, as well as its versatility as precursor in the synthesis of ^{11}C labeled physiologically active substrates and drugs. The two dominant modes of ^{11}C production include deuteron or proton bombardment of a molten boric oxide target, $^{10}B(d,n)^{11}C$, $^{11}B(d,2n)^{11}C$ or $^{11}B(p,n)^{11}C$; or proton bombardment of nitrogen gas, $^{14}N(p,α)^{11}C$.

A flow system for production of ^{11}C *via* the $^{14}N(p,α)^{11}C$ reaction appears in Figure 4. In the past, B_2O_3 target systems were the more commonly used for ^{11}C production[19-22] but with the continuing installation of many new accelerators in biomedical facilities the relatively simple targetry and higher production rates have made the latter nuclear route to ^{11}C more attractive.[42,54-56]

While the details of target design and development are outside of the scope of this discussion, it is appropriate to note that with B_2O_3 target systems the molten state of the target material permits effective diffusion of a $^{11}CO/^{11}CO_2$ mixture out of the melt for its removal by a sweep gas. Special effort in design is required to retain the liquid B_2O_3 in the beam. Both static and flowing gas systems are used and, particularly in the flow systems, pressure, flow rate, and composition of the sweep gas can have a substantial effect on the yield and chemical form of recovered ^{11}C. Usually, the use of complex sweep gasses is avoided since activation of the added components can lead to contamination by unwanted radionuclides.

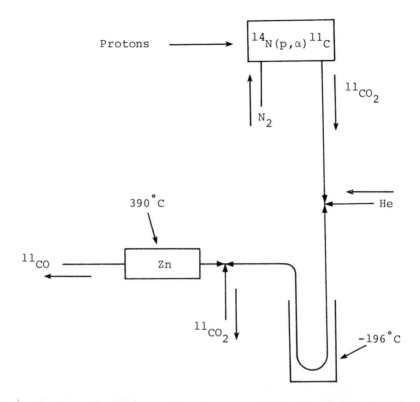

FIGURE 4. ^{11}C-Labeled CO_2 and CO production using the $^{14}N(p,\alpha)^{11}C$ nuclear reaction in a flowing gas target system.

The use of an inert sweep gas, such as He, results in the recovery of essentially pure $^{11}CO_2$ from the B_2O_3 target systems.[21] This is attributed to radiolytic oxidation of ^{11}CO produced within the target. Inclusion of a few percent of CO in the inert sweep gas results in recovery of an appreciable fraction of the ^{11}C in the form of ^{11}CO. The reduction in ^{11}C specific activity is significant and substantial amounts of $^{11}CO_2$ are still present. A more attractive approach is to substitute H_2 as the sweep gas; in which case the majority of the recovered radioactivity is in the form of ^{11}CO. Using either approach, radiochemically pure ^{11}CO is subsequently produced by removing the undesired $^{11}CO_2$ with an appropriate absorber such as soda lime.

If the $^{14}N(p,\alpha)^{11}C$ nuclear reaction is used for ^{11}C production, once again either a flow or static target system can be used.[42,54-56] In the case of flow systems, the N_2 gas serves as both target and sweep gas. With static systems, release of N_2 pressure from the target and any convenient sweep gas is used for recovery of ^{11}C. With either such target systems, experience has shown that even the use of very high purity N_2 (99.999%) results in recovery of $^{11}CO_2$ in almost quantitative yields, although passage of the ^{11}C labeled effluent gas from the target through a CuO furnace at 800°C assures total conversion of any ^{11}CO present to $^{11}CO_2$. Presumably, as with the B_2O_3 target system, the addition of a small fraction of CO to the N_2 target gas would result in recovery of some ^{11}C in the form of CO. However, the use of on stream reduction of $^{11}CO_2$ in a Zn furnace at 390°C has proven to be a reliable, convenient method for high yield, high-specific activity production of ^{11}CO.

Processing systems for recovery of ^{11}C in the form of HCN have been developed for both the B_2O_3 and N_2 target systems.[22,42,56] For either static or flow targets, the inert target effluent containing ^{11}C is mixed with H_2 and is passed over a Ni catalyst at 400°C where $^{11}CH_4$ is

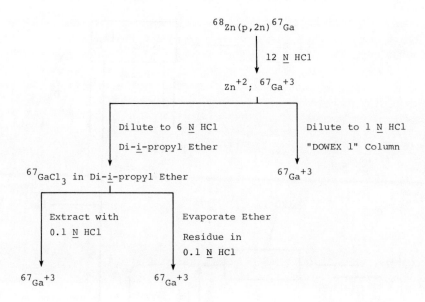

FIGURE 5.   Radiochemical processing of ^{67}Ga by solvent extraction and column chromatography.

produced. Ammonia is injected into the product gas stream, which then passes over a Pt catalyst at 950°C where ^{11}C labeled HCN is produced in high yield. Large quantities of H^{11}CN can be produced ''on stream'' by proton bombardment of a 95% N$_2$/5% H$_2$ gas mixture. The ^{11}CH$_4$ which is recovered from the target is routed through a Pt furnace as described above. The NH$_3$ which is required for conversion of ^{11}CH$_4$ to H^{11}CN is generated radiolytically from the target gas itself.

A variety of additional ^{11}C labeled intermediates which are useful in organic syntheses can be produced *via* additional processing of ^{11}C.[44,57-60] The examples cited above summarize only the simplest aspects of this area.

C. Gallium-67

Gallium-67 has proven to be an important radionuclide which is useful in nuclear medicine procedures for the detection of a variety of malignancies.[61-63] The radiochemical processing involved in the production of ^{67}Ga is representative of that used for many different types of transition metal radionuclides. The most common nuclear reactions which are used to produce ^{67}Ga involve either proton or deutron bombardment of Zn.[64,65] If either particle is used to irradiate a natural Zn target, substantial amounts of ^{66}Ga (9.3 hr half-life) are produced via the ^{66}Zn(d,2n)^{66}Ga and ^{66}Zn(p,n)^{66}Ga reactions. The use of enriched ^{68}Zn target material results in a substantial reduction of ^{66}Ga contamination while providing high yields of ^{67}Ga. Using 98% enriched ^{68}Zn as an internal target irradiated with 30 MeV protons a yield of 4.5 mCi/μAr, with 3% ^{66}Ga contamination, has been reported.[65]

The high chemical reactivity of Zn facilitates easy dissolution of the target in HCl. If the target material has been electroplated onto a Cu support, as is frequently the case, the support material does not dissolve. Separation of ^{67}Ga from the target material and radionuclidic contaminants can then be achieved either by solvent extraction or ion exchange chromatography. These alternative approaches are outlined in Figure 5.

If solvent extraction is used, high radiochemical purity can be achieved by diluting the HCl solution of dissolved irradiated target to 7 N and extracting it with diisopropyl ether. Under these conditions, the radiogallium is present as GaCl$_3$, which extracts into the organic phase. The ^{67}Ga is then converted to an aqueous solution by either back extracting the diiosoprophyl ether with dilute HCl, or by evaporating the organic solvent and redissolving the residue in dilute HCl. Chemical purity of the product can be determined by radionuclidic analysis for Zn radionuclides. The simplicity of this approach has made it attractive for both research and routine production purposes. In the latter case, several Ci of ^{67}Ga may be processed at any one time and provision for remote manipulations is essential.

If column chromatography is used to process the activated Zn target, anion exchange resins in the chloride form are invariably used, since $ZnCl_4^{-2}$-forms essentially quantitatively in 1 M chloride solutions and is retained on the resin column, while the radiogallium, which does not form an anionic complex under these conditions, passes through. The target is dissolved in dilute HCl and the chloride ion concentration of the resulting solution is adjusted to 1 M. If 1 N HCl is used for dissolving the activated target, no adjustment is required. The resulting solution is then applied to the top of a 2.0 cm ID × 5 cm column of strong anion exchanger which has been pre-equilibrated with 1 N HCl. The Zn is retained as the anionic chloride complex while the ^{67}Ga passes through. The resulting HCl solution is then evaporated to dryness and the residue is taken up in dilute HCl. If the nuclear reactions involved in production give rise to radiogermanium contamination, the Ge isotopes are conveniently removed by use of a simple Al_2O_3 column in tandem with the resin column.[64]

While either of these processing schemes can be adapted for use with other gallium radionuclides, it is important to realize that the use of anion exchangers to separate various anionic metal complexes, particularly complex chlorides, is a standard approach that offers great versatility. The processing of Zn radionuclides produced using Cu targets, and subsequent application of the ^{62}Zn in a ^{62}Cu generator based upon complex anion formation has been reported.[66,67]

VII. CONCLUSION

Clearly, the selection or development of an "appropriate" radiochemical processing scheme can be a complex and relatively difficult task. A variety of illustrative and alternative approaches to the various steps involved have been outlined. A few representative processing schemes have been examined in some detail. While these examples may serve to highlight the skills and versatility of the radiochemist, the most difficult aspect of radiochemical processing is frequently found in reconciling the trade-offs which were illustrated in Figure 1. If the proper facilities are available, and the intended application and the limitations which that application impose on product quality are understood, a safe and reliable "appropriate" radiochemical processing scheme can almost always be developed. In the absence of such an understanding, even the best of facilities and technical skills are no guarantee of success.

REFERENCES

1. **Ballantine, D. S.,** Preparation of carrier-free iodine, *Natl. Nucl. Energy Ser.,* 9, 1639, 1951.
2. **Case, F. N. and Acree, E. H.,** Large scale preparation of high purity I-131 and Xe-133 by sorption techniques, U.S.A.E.C. Report ORNL-3840, Oak Ridge, Tenn., 1966, 15 pages.
3. **Glendenin, L. E. and Metcalf, R. P.,** Characteristics of 6.7 hr I-135, *Natl. Nucl. Energy Ser.,* 9, 992, 1951.
4. **Katcoff, S., Dillard, C. R., Finston, H., et al.,** Determination of fission iodine in uranium metal, *Natl. Nucl. Energy Ser.,* 9, 1635, 1951.

5. **Kenny, A. W. and Spragg, W. T.,** Extraction of carrier-free ^{131}I from pile irradiated Te, *J. Chem. Soc.,* S323, 1949.

6. **Kraus, K. A. and Moore, G. E.,** Anion-exchange studies. V. Bivalent transition metals Mn to Zn in HCl, *J. Am. Chem. Soc.,* 75, 1460, 1953.

7. **Bonner, O. D. and Smith, L. L.,** A selectivity scale for some bivalent cations on Dowex-50, *J. Chem. Phys.,* 61, 326, 1957.

8. **Herber, R. H. and Irvine, J. W.,** Anion-exchange studies. I. Bromide complexes of Co(II), Cu(II), Zn(II), and Ga(III), *J. Am. Chem. Soc.,* 76, 987, 1954.

9. **Szilard, L. and Chalmers, T. A.,** Chemical separation of the radioactive element from its bombarded isotope in the Fermi effect, *Nature (London),* 134, 462, 1934.

10. **Pauly, J. and Sue, P.,** Recoil of P^{30} atoms from the nuclear reaction $P^{31}(\alpha,n)^{30}P$ — application to the preparation of carrier-free P^{30}, *Compt. Rend.,* 240, 2226, 1955.

11. **Harvey, B. G.,** Recoil techniques in nuclear reaction and fission studies, *Ann. Rev. Nucl. Sci.,* 10, 235, 1960.

12. **Wolf, A. P.,** The reactions of energetic tritium and carbon atoms with organic compounds, *Adv. Phys. Org. Chem.,* 2, 201, 1964.

13. **Kusaka, Y. and Meinke, W.,** Rapid radiochemical separations, *Nucl. Sci. Ser.,* (NAS-NS 3104), 1961.

14. **Freiser, H. and Morrison, G. H.,** Solvent extraction in radiochemical separations, *Ann. Rev. Nucl. Sci.,* 9, 221, 1959.

15. **Snell, A. H., Levinger, J. S., Meiners, E. P., et al.,** Studies of the delayed neutrons. II. Chemical isolation of the 56-second and 23-second activities, *Phys. Rev.,* 72, 545, 1947.

16. **Blue, J. W., Leonard, R., Jha, S., et al.,** A cyclotron target for the production of radioxenons, *Progr. Nucl. Med.,* 4, 53, 1978.

17. **Perrier, C. and Segre, E.,** Chemical properties of element 43, *J. Chem. Phys.,* 5, 712, 1937.

18. **Boyd, R. E.,** Recent developments in generators of Tc-99m, in *Radiopharmaceuticals and Labelled Compounds,* Vol. 1, I.A.E.A., Vienna, 1973, 3.

19. **Vonberg, D. D., Baker, L. C., Buckingham, P. D., et al.,** Target system for radioisotope production on the Medical Research Council cyclotron, in *Uses of Cyclotrons in Chemistry Metallurgy, and Biology,* Amphlett, C. B., Ed., Butterworths, London, 1970, 258.

20. **Welch, M. J. and Ter-Pogossian, M. M.,** Preparation of short half-lived radioactive gases for medical studies, *Radiation Res.,* 36, 580, 1968.

21. **Clark, J. C. and Buckingham, P. D.,** Carbon-11, in *Short-Lived Radioactive Gases for Clinical Use,* Butterworths, London, 1975, 215.

22. **Washburn, L. C., Sun, T. T., Byrd, B. L., et al.,** High-level production of C-11-carboxyl-labeled amino acids, in *Radiopharmaceuticals II,* Sodd, V. J., Allen, D. R., Hoogland, D. R., and Ice, R. D., Eds., Society of Nuclear Medicine, New York, 1979, 767.

23. **Krohn, K. A. and Jansholt, A.-L.,** Radiochemical quality control of short-lived radiopharmaceuticals, *Int. J. Appl. Radiat. Isotopes,* 28, 213, 1977.

24. **Cohen, Y. and Besnard, M.,** Analytical methods of radiopharmaceutical quality control, in *Radiopharmaceuticals,* Subramanian, G., Rhodes, B., Cooper, J., and Sodd, V., Eds., Society of Nuclear Medicine, New York, 1975, 207.

25. *Analytical Control of Radiopharmaceuticals,* I.A.E.A., Vienna, 1970.

26. **Zielinski, F. W., Holly, F. E., Robinson, G. D., et al.,** Total and individual kidney function assessment with iodine-123 orthoiodohippurate, *Radiology,* 125, 753, 1977.

27. **Zielinski, F. W., MacDonald, N. S., Robinson, G. D., et al.,** Compact cyclotron production of radiochemically pure I-123 iodode for synthesis of radiodiagnostic agents, *J. Nucl. Med.,* 18, 67, 1977.

28. **Eckelman, W. C. and Richards, P.,** Analytical pitfalls with Tc-99m-labeled compounds, *J. Nucl. Med.,* 13, 202, 1972.

29. **Kristensen, K.,** Quality control analysis at the hospital, in *Radiopharmaceuticals II,* Sodd, V., Allen, D., Hoogland, D., and Ice, R., Eds., Society of Nuclear Medicine, New York, 1979, 1.

30. **Castronovo, F. P.,** Principles, properties, and quality control of nuclear medicine agents, in *Nuclear Medicine Physics, Instrumentation, and Agents,* Rollo, F. D., Ed., C. V. Mosby, St. Louis, 1977, 560.

31. **Bida, G., Ehrenkaufer, R., Wolf, A. P., et al.,** The effect of target gas purity on the chemical form of ^{18}F during ^{18}F-F_2 production using the neon-fluorine (Ne/F_2) target, *J. Nucl. Med.,* 21, 758, 1980.

32. **Dahl, J. R. and Tilbury, R. S.,** The use of compact, multi-particle cyclotron for the production of ^{52}Fe, ^{67}Ga, ^{111}In, and ^{123}I for medical purposes, *Int. J. Appl. Radiat. Isotopes,* 23, 431, 1972.

33. **Brown, L. C. and Beats, A. L.,** Cyclotron production of carrier-free indium-111, *Int. J. Appl. Radiat. Isotopes,* 23, 57, 1972.

34. **Thakur, M. L. and Nunn, A. D.,** Cyclotron produced indium-111 for medical use, *Int. J. Appl. Radiat. Isotopes,* 23, 139, 1972.

35. **Thakur, M. L.,** Gallium-67 and indium-111 radiopharmaceuticals, *Int. J. Appl. Radiat. Isotopes,* 28, 183, 1977.

36. **Phillips, J. P.,** The reactions of 8-quinolinol., *Chem. Res.,* 56, 271, 1956.
37. **Thakur, M. L. and Gottschalk, A.,** Role of radiopharmaceuticals in nuclear hematology, in *Radiopharmaceuticals II,* Allen, D., Hoogland, D., Sodd, V., and Ice, R., Eds., Society of Nuclear Medicine, New York, 1979, 341.
38. **Casella, V., Ido, T., Wolf, A. P., et al,** Anhydrous ^{18}F-F$_2$ for radiopharmaceutical preparation, *J. Nucl. Med.,* 21, 750, 1980.
39. **Fowler, J. S., Finn, R. D., Lambrecht, R. M., et al.,** The synthesis of 5-F-18-fluorouracil, *J. Nucl. Med.,* 14, 63, 1973.
40. **Robinson, G. D., MacDonald, N. S., Easton, M. P., et al.,** F-18 fluorodeoxyglucose: Remote, semiautomated production using a compact cyclotron, *J. Nucl. Med.,* 19, 701, 1978.
41. **Wolf, A. P. and Fowler, J. S.,** Organic radiopharmaceuticals: recent advances, in *Radiopharmaceuticals II,* Sodd, V., Allen, D., Hoogland, D., and Ice, R., Eds., Society of Nuclear Medicine, New York, 1979, 73.
42. **Christman, D. R., Finn, R. D., Karlstrom, K. I., et al.,** The production of ultra high activity ^{11}C-labeled hydrogen cyanide, carbon dioxide, carbon monoxide, and methane via the [14]N(p,α)[11]C reaction, *Int. J. Appl. Radiat. Isotopes,* 26, 435, 1975.
43. **Williams, D. L., Finn, R. D., Campbell, J. A., et al.,** Thallium-201: physical properties and methods of production, in *Thallium-201 Myocardial Imaging,* Ritchie, J., Hamilton, G., and Wackers, F., Eds., Raven Press, New York, 1978, chap. 10.
44. **Marazano, C., Maziere, M., Berger, G., et al.,** Automated synthesis of ^{11}C-labelled radiopharmaceuticals: imipramine, chlorpromazine, nicotine and methionine, *Int. J. Appl. Radiat. Isotopes,* 30, 393, 1979.
45. **Barrio, J. R., MacDonald, N. S., Robinson, G. D., et al.,** Remote, semiautomated production of F-18-labeled 2-deoxy-2-fluoro-D-glucose, *J. Nucl. Med.,* 22, 372, 1981.
46. **Fowler, J. S., MacGregor, R. R., Wolf, A. P., et al.,** A shielded synthesis system for production of 2-deoxy-2-[18F]-fluoro-D-glucose, *J. Nucl. Med.,* 22, 376, 1981.
47. ORNL Radioisotopes Production Manuel, Case, F. N., Ed., U.S.A.E.C. Report ORNL-3633, Oak Ridge, Tenn., 1964, 217 pages.
48. **Hupf, H. B.,** Production and purification of radionuclides, in *Radiopharmacy,* Tubis, M. and Wolf, W., Eds., John Wiley & Sons, New York, 1976, 225.
49. **Evans, C. and Stevenson, J.,** British Patent 763, 865 19.12.56., United Kingdom Atomic Energy Authority.
50. **Fusco, M. S., Peek, N. F., Jungermann, J. A., et al.,** Production of carrier free ^{123}I using the [127]I(p,5n)[123]Xe reaction, *J. Nucl. Med.,* 13, 729, 1972.
51. **Lindner, L., Brinkman, G., Suer, T., et al.,** Accelerator production of ^{18}F, [123]Xe(^{123}I), [211]At, and [38]S, in *Radiopharmaceuticals and Labelled Compounds,* Vol. 1, I.A.E.A., Vienna, 1973, 303.
52. **Bievelez, P., Cogneau, M., Charlier, R., et al.,** Preparation of carrier-free iodine-123 with a high radionuclidic purity, *J. Radioanalyt. Chem.,* 30, 67, 1976.
53. **Cunninghame, J. D., Morris, B., Nichols, A. L., et al.,** Large scale production of ^{123}I from a flowing liquid target using the (p,5n) reaction, *Int. J. Appl. Radiat. Isotopes,* 27, 597, 1976.
54. **Finn, R. D. and Wolf, A. P.,** Cyclotron production of ^{11}C-carbon dioxide from a nitrogen gas target, *J. Nucl. Med.,* 13, 429, 1972.
55. **Lamb, J. F., James, R. W., and Winchell, H. S.,** Recoil synthesis of high specific activity ^{11}C-cyanide, *Int. J. Appl. Radiat. Isotopes,* 22, 1475, 1971.
56. **Christman, D. R., Finn, R. D., Karlstrom, K. I., et al.,** Production of carrier-free H[11]CN for medical use and radiopharmaceutical syntheses. IX, *J. Nucl. Med.,* 14, 864, 1973.
57. **Myers, W. G.,** ^{11}C-Acetylene, *J. Nucl. Med.,* 13, 699, 1972.
58. **Winstead, M. B., Chern, C. N., Lin, T. H., et al.,** Synthesis and preliminary scintigraphic evaluation of *in vivo* distribution of ^{11}C-hydroxyurea/isohydroxyurea and ^{11}C-cyanide, *Int. J. Appl. Radiat. Isotopes,* 29, 443, 1978.
59. **Brinkman, C. A., Hass-Lisewska, I., Veenboer, J. T., et al.,** Preparation of [11]COCl$_2$, *Int. J. Appl. Radiat. Isotopes,* 29, 701, 1978.
60. **Marazano, C., Maziere, M., Berger, G., et al.,** Synthesis of methyl iodide-^{11}C and formaldehyde-^{11}C, *Int. J. Appl. Radiat. Isotopes,* 28, 49, 1977.
61. **Turner, D. A., Pinsky, S. M., Gottschalk, A., et al.,** The use of ^{67}Ga scanning in the staging of Hodgkins' disease, *Radiology,* 104, 97, 1972.
62. **Greenlaw, R. H., Weinstein, M. B., Brill, A. B., et al.,** ^{67}Ga-citrate imaging in untreated malignant lymphoma: preliminary report of cooperative group, *J. Nucl. Med.,* 15, 404, 1974.
63. **Deland, F. H., Sauerbrunn, B. J. L., Boyd, C., et al.,** ^{67}Ga-citrate imaging in untreated primary lung cancer: preliminary report of cooperative group, *J. Nucl. Med.,* 15, 408, 1974.,
64. **Beaver, J. E., Bolomey, L., Nash, D., et al.,** Radionuclide production aspects of a CS-30 cyclotron, *Prog. Nucl. Med.,* 4, 28, 1978.

65. **Helus, F. and Maier-Borst, W.,** A comparative investigation of methods used to produce ^{67}Ga with a cyclotron, in *Radiopharmaceuticals and Labelled Compounds*, Vol 1, I.A.E.A., Vienna, 1973, 317.

66. **Robinson, G. D.,** Cyclotron related radiopharmaceutical development program at UCLA, *Prog. Nucl. Med.*, 4, 80, 1978.

67. **Robinson, G. D., Lee, A. W., and Zielinski, F. W.,** The zinc-62/copper-62 generator: a convenient source of copper-62 for radiopharmaceuticals, *Int. J. Appl. Radiat. Isotopes*, 31, 111, 1980.

INDEX